D1598755

RE-CREATION

SURVIVING THE HUMAN EXPERIENCE

KRISTIN AURELIA

SHE Wise Publications, LLC
www.shewisepublications.com

Kristin Aurelia/ SHE Wise Publications, LLC
Brandywine, MD 20613
www.shewisepublications.com

RE-CREATION Surviving the Human Experience/ Kristin Aurelia —1st ed.
ISBN 979-8-9883416-0-4

Contents

Part One- Anna's Story 1

Part Two- Re-Creation Reflections..56

Part Three- A Quest for Discovering the Truth 95

DEDICATION

This book is dedicated to all of the amazing human beings on this planet who have gone through, are going through, or are continuing to go through, the human experience in search of greater meaning and understanding. Sometimes the answers are not as complicated as they seem. They just require some soul searching and walking the spiritual path to experience a true Awakening and to live in YOUR individual truth.

I would like to thank God for giving me the strength and courage to take this journey. Thank you for always loving me through my ups and downs. You have never left me, during the good and not so good moments, and always loved me unconditionally. You have provided life lessons, growth opportunities, and kept pushing me to become more, evolve more and be my best self, even when I wanted to push back. In my darkest moments, it was my Faith that got me through, and I am forever grateful for your unconditional divine love!

Special appreciation and gratitude go out to my family for their love and support as I have gone through this journey. I know it has not been easy, as you have seen me at my best and my worst, and still continue to love me through it. My Mom has held space for me as I continued to "find myself" and "find my way." To my incredible children, God has blessed me with the most loving, gentle, kindhearted and spiritual beings a mom could ever ask for. I am honored to be given the great responsibility to walk through life with each of you. You have stuck by me, watched me soar, watched me fall apart, piece myself back together, and loved me through every step of the journey.

A heart-felt thanks to the many spiritual teachers and guides, both physical and non-physical, who have been instrumental in my spiritual journey and continuous growth. God has placed each and every one of you in my life at different stages and phases throughout the awakening and healing process, and I am forever grateful and thankful for all of the knowledge, wisdom and love shared. Surviving the human experience is truly a process and it is through love and support along the way that this journey has been met with more ease and clarity.

I would be remiss if I did not acknowledge all of the individuals in my life, who have entered my life for a season or for a reason. There have been so many who have had such a profound impact along the way. To my energy healers, my soul humans, and those who have left an imprint on my soul, in both positive and not so positive ways...you are loved and cherished. To those who have taught me the tough lessons of heartbreak, betrayal, distrust and so many other unpleasant human experiences, your purpose was served. There were so many memories created lessons that were taught, and messages delivered. Without all of these experiences, the good, the bad and the ugly, I would not be who I am today. I have learned to love, the true meaning of self-love, truth, authenticity, forgiveness, empathy, understanding, unconditional love and so much more! So, for that, I am ap-appreciative that God has walked with me through the tumultuous journey and has held my hand as I continued to awaken and experience my truth...the evolution of my mind, body and soul.

INTRODUCTION

RE-CREATION – SURVIVING THE HUMAN EXPERIENCE is a unique book that takes the reader on a journey through Anna's dark past she never realized existed. She uncovers a life filled with deceit and abusive relationships. Anna became so beaten down and overwhelmed that she actually encounters a near death experience. It took all of these experiences for her to recognize how she lost herself trying to please others. At this point, Anna embarks on a mission to heal the physical and emotional damage as well as the trauma that plagued her for the better part of her life. She spends several years on her quest to reconnect her mind, body and soul. Anna shares so much knowledge which she gained along her path to help others see that there is a way to overcome all odds and restore love and light in the world. She shares her story, in the hope that others will begin their journey to find their personal truth, move closer to the light, discover and live out their intended purpose here on Earth.

Part 1 – Anna's Story. This section of the book is designed to take the reader on a journey and share Anna's story through darkness and her metamorphosis and transformation to the light. She seeks answers and to understand the secrets and keys to restoring her health, healing and awakening. She does not realize in the beginning that she is in for a life-changing experience that is beyond her physical human form's comprehension. The experiences and answers she finds along the way lead her to find deeper meaning, TRUTH and a deeper connection with her maker...GOD! She shares her story in an effort to assist the reader in understanding where it all begins. Although her story may be somewhat unique, the journey she embarks upon is not unique to the soul's process of going through an awakening and awareness of what is and what is not living in TRUTH.

Part 2 – Re-Creation Reflections. This section of the book goes through a series of reflections and explorations. As Anna goes through her journey, she is charged with asking herself tough questions and exploring her human-form's life narrative. Throughout this process, she reflects upon her childhood, her belief systems formed through life experiences and limiting beliefs resulting from these experiences. She uses a myriad of strategies, to walk through the fire and depths of darkness that have plagued her soul, to find her voice and power. Also, she explores a series of questions that have been a topic of discussion for mankind for centuries. Her approach to answering these questions leads her on traditional and non- traditional paths to seek out the answers. Her Spiritual Awakening leads her to explore and embrace the Spiritual, non- physical, transcendental, energy healing, universal law and homeopathic lifestyle. It is through this newfound perspective, Anna encounters many amazing teachers, protocols, remedies and is introduced to so many tools that are very different than anything she had tried before. Her experiences lead her to an amazing group of Spiritual guides, who teach her healing practices using her own power and inner strength to heal her mind, body, spirit and soul beyond anything modern traditional methodologies could offer.

Part 3 – A Quest for Discovering the Truth, dives deeply into the most sought-after answers from a spiritual and unspoken place of healing. In this section of the book, Anna introduces some of the strategies, methodologies and guides that aided her on her journey and brought restored and renewed Faith, hope, love, energy and truth into her withering soul. Through trial and error, she explored a variety of tools and techniques and worked with many healers who provided knowledge and an environment for her to grow. Anna is able to explore her inner darkness and reignite the light inside her soul so that she can find the strength to rescue herself from the damage caused by the chaos, toxicity and remnants of trauma that had slowly eaten away at her mind, body and spirit over time.

This healing was necessary for her to ensure the human form could reconnect with her soul can get back on track, back to doing what she was placed on this Earth to do...GOD'S WORK. In this section of the book, the format is slightly different. It transitions from a story mode to a learning mode, exploring topics, questions and answers with the intent to provide clarity, messages of TRUTH, hope and healing.

I hope you enjoy the journey and will consider going on YOUR journey to restore your health, Faith, belief system and live out your authentic TRUTH!

PART ONE

ANNA'S STORY

HOW IT ALL BEGAN

Anna was loved by all she encountered! She had the ability to light up any room she walked into with her radiant smile. She was high-energy and her charisma brought people together everywhere she went. She was known as the social butterfly who could adapt in any environment or situation and was always able to fit in no matter where she went. She was well-versed in everything from launching world-wide programs on large scales to the masses to creating handmade potholders. She was a high-powered businesswoman who received many accolades for her accomplishments. Her love for her family was evident in all that she did. She lived and breathed to ensure her family was afforded all the opportunities that their hearts desired. She was a committed, faithful wife, who loved without judgement and would do anything for her spouse. She was a daughter, who spent her life always trying to achieve greatness in all that she did to make her parents proud. Overall, she was a well-adjusted, loved by all, overachiever, who made it her life's mission to always accomplish whatever task she had set out to do.

Behind this strong, vibrant, fiery individual was a woman who was doing her best to keep up with all of the endless demands of her time. To say her plate was full was an understatement. She was so focused on making sure everyone's needs were met that she failed to see that she was slowly draining her own cup. As time went on and the bar for expectations began to be set higher and higher, she felt increasing pressure to perform as she always had and unexpectedly, she felt her health slowly begin to decline. In the beginning, there were a few minor things, here and there, and then next her happiness began to slowly diminish. Her needs and happiness became lost in the demands of those who had benefited for so long from her delivery of 5-star service of whatever was needed at any given time. Slowly, her energy began to decline, the fatigue began to set in, and the inflammation in her body became evident. Then, the neurological symptoms began, and her cognitive functions were slowly beginning to decline. As her battery continued to drain, she quickly realized her body was not bouncing back like it used to in prior times. Re-charging seemed unachievable. All she knew was she needed to get it together, because there were a lot of people depending on her and she did not have time to be down.

About eight years prior to her awakening, Anna met a man, Lionel, at an event and was taken off guard by his interest in her. He was unlike anyone she had ever met before. At the conclusion of the evening, after a few drinks and laughs, they exchanged numbers and headed their separate ways. Soon after they scheduled several more dates and before she knew it, she had fallen madly in love with this exciting and mysterious man. She was on cloud nine and just knew he was the one. It was as if he was the male version of her. Anna was taken by surprise by his constant love, attention and affection. He literally swept her off her feet with all the surprise dates, trips and constant talk about their future. Although he was not big on kids, he appeared to embrace her children and showed interest in their lives. After years and years of being tossed aside by the men in her life, she had finally found someone who was treating her like a Queen and had opened her eyes to a world filled with fun, excitement and adventure. There were times that she would reflect and thought it was all too good to be true. How could she have stumbled across this man who seemed so perfect for her? Where had he been hiding all this time? Lionel had never been married before and had one child. He was quick-witted, charming and loved to have a good time. Could this really be happening? Could he really be this amazing? It was very much a pinch me moment...to confirm that this was all real.

The relationship progressed pretty quickly, much quicker than any other she had experienced. He would show up and surprise her with gifts and tickets to events she wanted to attend and some she had no clue about but grew to enjoy. Soon after, he asked her to move in because they were literally inseparable as the weeks and months progressed. It all seemed pretty practical and logical. A little over a year later, after living together, he took her on a whimsical trip and got on one knee and asked her to marry him. She was speechless...a dream come true and with that began an adventure she never could have seen coming. She spent the next year and a half planning their dream wedding. It was beyond anything she could have ever expected. As a child, most girls dream about their wedding day. What will it look like? What will the dress look like? Where will it be held? Anna had never put much thought into a wedding, and this was turning out to be the wedding she never knew she wanted. The adventures continued and she could not be surer of anything than wanting to spend the rest of her life with the man she had fallen completely in love with. As the wedding day drew closer, and she became increasingly distracted with the details, she started to notice the late nights out and she began to have some concerns about his whereabouts. She was not quite sure what was going on, but her intuition told her something seemed off and before she knew it, she had uncovered that this amazing man had been covering up his guy's night out with some end of evening trips to the strip clubs. He apparently had quite a nightlife that she did not know about until much later. Despite this concern, she thought maybe this was just a "right before marriage" single man's behavior and she continued to focus on the matter at hand...planning for the Big Day and the incredible future ahead.

Fast forward to present day...after the Big Day...her whole world changed. Lionel changed. He no longer was the loving sweet guy full of surprises and adoration for the woman he put so much work into courting in their early phases of the relationship. As the pressures continued to grow, she became increasingly fearful as she knew there was no room for error. She had in essence become the "YES" girl and saying "NO" to anything felt contradictory to her being and her character. She could not possibly let anything fall. Oh, and yes...it was absolutely necessary to keep that smile on her face, regardless of what was going on inside her body and mind. As she began to voice her concerns about what was going on, it fell on deaf ears. How could the woman who had held it together all these years be unable to keep performing her Super Woman duties? That just did not make sense. So, her cries for help went unnoticed.

Anna knew she could not keep up this act much longer. She soon began to find herself reaching for three cups of coffee a day at work versus her one cup just to stay awake. Then came the naps after work to try to get a quick recharge. She had to start delegating more of her high-level projects to her staff because she just could not find the strength to keep pushing through. Her husband slowly became more and more aggravated with her as he could not understand why she could not come home and go out, hangout and stay up until two or three am talking about worldly topics. He became increasingly frustrated and bored, as he required attention and stimulation twenty-four seven and he began to slowly start going out more and staying out later. The kids were at demanding ages and needed more and more attention as they were in that space of teen years where they were not quite grown up, but they were not babies either. This transition requires a different mental capacity and parenting demand than raising babies. Teen years are trying on their own, let alone several teens, all at once, with different life struggles, needs and requirements. As Anna continued to struggle, and just barely keep her head above water, there were still the daily life requirements she was expected to perform such as cooking, cleaning, working out to stay fit, because gaining weight was not acceptable to herself or her spouse. Oh, the pressure...she was slowly sinking, and everyone just looked at her like "What the hell are you doing? What is wrong with you?" She quickly learned that there was no room for error or grace for her...she had set the standards from day one and everyone expected her to continue status quo. The saying "be careful what you get people used to" had become the nightmare she was living.

Slowly, her heart began to break as she felt her dreams slipping through her fingers. The marriage she was so excited for, the man she adored and the home they had created began to crumble. She desperately tried everything to keep his affection. She would dress the way he liked, changed her looks, go on outlandish adventures and more. Self-help books, Podcasts, YouTube videos and therapy were her strategies to solving the problems that continued to grow. It was as if nothing she did was right and she kept trying harder and harder and it got worse and worse.

Lionel soon began taking trips without her. He would do things with his child and exclude her children. He even scheduled a trip with his child and basically told the family he just wanted to go on a trip alone with his child. Talk about a blow to the other children who looked up to him as a father figure. One evening during an argument over what he thought the kids should be doing, the kids asked him if he even wanted them there and he said he was fifty/fifty about having a family. He said it was much easier when he was by himself.

Lionel picked at everything from Anna's cooking to the way her kids were being raised to what she should be doing to fix the marriage. He would reach out to her family and deliberately demean Anna for what he thought she should be doing and how she should be acting. He painted the picture of her as if she were an unruly wife who was fragile and incapable of making decisions for herself or the family. It did not matter what she did...it was not enough.

The writing was on the wall and there was nothing she could do, because all she had done to build the home, she so desperately desired was all a facade. It was as if Anna and Lionel were living two different lives. Despite the pain and heartache, she felt, she had made a commitment before God and her husband, and she was giving her all and was losing the war. Regardless of how bad it continued to get, she was madly in love with him and adored everything about who she thought he was, and the reality was, he was not that man. He was clever and had found a way to mirror what she wanted and slowly over time, his mask began to slip and the TRUTH of who he really was started to show, and he was exposed. The heartbreak of this fantasy fairytale Anna had been living for years was more than her heart, mind and soul could bear. It was devastating. She knew that she could not turn back the hands of time or unsee what she had seen.

Throughout this process of discovery, the kids were just muddling through, and Anna could see them struggling to understand what was happening to their family and their mom. They became increasingly worried and reached out to their grandparents for help. They knew something was wrong and just did not know what was happening or how to fix it. Their schoolwork and social activities began to feel the effects of the chaos that was brewing at home. It was during this time that anxieties became heightened, and tension began to fester. What made this whole situation worse was the pandemic was brewing, and during a portion of the unraveling, they were all confined to the home due to the public health crisis.

On more than one occasion, Lionel would pick fights with the kids, and he specifically would pick at and attack Anna's oldest child to the point where he had gotten physical on more than one occasion. Locked away in their homes where everyone became very isolated was the perfect storm for what was happening behind closed doors. Anna could not bear to watch this behavior and had stepped in to defend her child, which had added fuel to the fire.

Eventually, the kids had enough and pulled Anna aside and had a "Come to Jesus" moment with their mother. They knew their mom was slowly falling apart, she was not happy, and her health was severely impacted. There were so many times that Lionel would attack the kids and tell them that they were the cause of their mother's health issues. After repeated demeaning conversations they began to believe it and they withdrew, because they just did not know what to do. It was becoming very obvious that their mom was being emotionally and mentally abused and they just could not stand to watch it anymore. Their mother was so very important to them, and they knew they could not sit back and allow this to continue. It was during that conversation that Anna realized that this was bigger than her. Her so-called happiness in this relationship, this marriage that was built on lies, this relationship that was based on the "benefit of her" and not the "love of her," was becoming clearer. Anna had to reach into her last bit of strength that she had in reserve and if she could not do this for herself, she had to do it for her kids. Everything she had done her whole life centered around giving her kids the best life that she could possibly give them. The reality was...this was not it! This was toxic, unhealthy and literally sucking the life out of her physical body. She decided she needed to put aside this nightmare and free herself and her children from the chains that were claiming her life. She owed that to her children and to herself!

It was not long after she came to this realization that her spouse started a heated argument, which had become the norm over the past few months. Lionel would create huge arguments as a distraction to deflect from what was really going on and he used it as a control mechanism to get her to "obey" his rules. On more than one occasion, he would refer to the podcasts and YouTube videos from relationship influencers who were on the male chauvinistic spectrum to let her know how a wife is supposed to behave. During this particular argument, he went a little too far and said he was tired of her not listening and doing as she was told. He looked at her and said, "I do not know why you have to be so strong, and you cannot just listen to your husband." It was at that moment that she knew this marriage was a farce and the feelings she had so deeply shared and poured into him the past several years were not reciprocal and she was living in her own delusional fantasy.

She assumed he loved her as she had been loving him; however, the truth was…he was making a mockery of her to his friends and family. They all knew he did not care about her. As he shared with them, she made him look good and if he ever got married, just know that it was a scam. The reality was, he was using her for his own personal benefit, simply another business transaction that made financial sense to him and greased his pockets. The truth was, he would often tell Anna and the kids that you should not love something that cannot love you back, as that was the mentality he was raised under. Not realizing what was really meant by this statement, Anna soon came to realize that love was something he was not capable of, as the only one he truly loved was himself and the only things he loved more than himself were money and power. He ruled his life, family and business based off of his need for money and power and anything that did not give him both was quickly removed. Once Anna fell ill, her value to him quickly decreased and that is when the tables really started to turn. He made a point of making it known to others that when she fell ill that he did not sign up for this.

When the fight happened that evening, in that very moment, she decided it was time for her and her children to leave. She made the tough choice to reflect back on the words of her children and be brutally honest with herself. She knew she deserved better, was worthy of so much more, and she could not believe she had allowed herself to give all of her power away to someone who had conned her into believing he had her best interest at heart. She and her children were just pawns in his game of chess. This was a game she could no longer afford to play, as it was close to claiming her life and she knew there was so much more in store for her. GOD had a plan, and it certainly was not for her to waste her life away being less than, living less than and being isolated from the world and abused. She was much too powerful, strong and capable and this was not going to be the end of her story.

Anna could not get out of her own way fast enough, so GOD made sure she was given a little nudge. This relationship and its toll on her had gone way too far and GOD could not stand by idly and watch one of his precious children be destroyed at the merciless hands of evil, power, money and greed. In the world of good versus evil, good always wins and it was time...time to end the chaos...the drama...the insanity. GOD had decided it was time for Him to step in and remind her of who she truly was and that her purpose is so much greater than what she was doing.

As she exited the relationship, her human form fell apart. This was all beyond comprehension to her. Her whole world felt like it was pulled out from under her, and the darkness set in. She felt herself feeling lost, empty and as if her dreams had just disappeared. This is where she began to experience the dark night of the soul and it was very painful. There was so much grief, sadness and a general sense of feeling completely lost. The death of her marriage was too much to bear.

Anna had no idea what to do next. She found herself in an apartment with her kids looking at one another and feeling a sense of gratefulness and thankfulness for making it out of the unhealthy, abusive, toxic relationship, but she missed him, she missed the man she thought he was and she missed the life and future she thought she would have for the rest of her life. How could this have happened? Why...why did this happen? What a cruel joke this had been. Why would someone be so evil? What was the end game? It was not just her...she had beautiful children that were her life, and they too were affected. Why did it have to end this way? Why?

In true fashion, Anna began trying to dissect and make sense of what was going on. It was the only way she knew how to cope with her world falling apart. If she could just find an explanation. Was this a lesson? Did she do something wrong? Why did he not want her the way he did for the years before they were wed? Why was she not enough? Why the sneaking around with other women? Why the lies? Why the fake promises? Why did he toy with her mind and emotions? Why was he not affected by what he had done to her and her children? Did he have no conscience? Why was he so cold...so empty and void of empathy? Why did she hurt so much? Why could she not just get it together? She is strong...why...why...why!

As she tried to find the answers, she realized they were not going to be provided. Sometimes you just cannot make sense of evil or the destruction and insanity that unfolds as a result. Sometimes you just have to get on your knees and pray and know that the Big Guy heard and saw things that we did not, and we get truly saved by the Grace of God. This was one of those moments in her life.

It was during this time of reflection she realized what had happened. As she turned to God searching for answers, she stumbled across a book that explained it clear as day. The book was, *Woman Evolve*, by Sarah Jakes Roberts.

As she listened to chapter after chapter in the audio book, it all began to make sense. The story of Adam and Eve played out and there it was...the story of Eve and the Serpent. The Serpent was so clever, and he had misled her. Everything about her relationship was a fantasy, an illusion and a figment of her imagination. She had wanted to be loved so desperately. She wanted to be enough...to feel special...to have the love of a lifetime and know that she mattered to someone.

Lionel knew all of this about her as he had so many deep conversations with her and knew her mind. It was not very hard for him to know her innermost thoughts as she remained completely vulnerable with him all the time and was like an open book. She was transparent and did not have anything to hide. He had studied her and learned her inside and out. He knew just what needed to happen to achieve his goals of getting whatever he wanted whenever he wanted, because he knew she was so over the moon for him that she would walk to the end of the Earth for him. Once she was able to put the life, she was living into the terms of the Biblical stories of Eve in the garden she quickly realized she had gotten played. She had been a fool in love who let her guard down and had fallen for the Serpent. This was such a hard realization to come to as she was still going through the stages of grief from the loss of her marriage. As she walked through those stages of grief, she sat in denial, and moving past this space was crucial as it would be pivotal in her healing journey.

This realization of what had happened caused Anna to decide that it was time to dive deeper into her heart and soul and she swore to never put herself in this position again. It was at that moment of realization that she became determined to strengthen her relationship with God, because she realized that she could no longer do this alone. She had always believed in God, prayed every day, went to church and had shared her love of God with her children. She raised her babies to know God and give credit where credit is due. She came to realize there was a disconnect happening. Although she was praying and talking to God regularly, she was still down on this Earth doing her own thing and living life her way. If she wanted it, she went for it. She was doing things her way...versus being in alignment with what was for her. This is where the real work began. Anna could no longer run or hide. It was time to roll up her sleeves and explore all things "Anna." Time to figure out who she really was under all this armor and all of these false beliefs she had adopted through years of trauma.

COMING UNDONE

Modern medicine had given up on Anna and so had her spouse. The family often would ask how she was doing, but she could feel that they thought she was making it up and that nothing was wrong. Her mother, children and best friend were the only ones who believed her. Everyone else had written her off as some fragile hot mess who was never "ok." The symptoms, onset and random unexplainable episodes, had become too much for everyone to keep track of and to comprehend. It was as if she was being treated like a woman who had gone mad...no medical explanation...so it must be in her head. She had even participated in therapy to rule out the possibility of having a mental illness. She was given a complete assessment and it was confirmed that all of her mental faculties were in place and that if anything, there was an extreme amount of stress in her life that could be the culprit of some of the unexplained things occurring.

The symptoms were so very real, the random feelings of tingling in her body, the partial paralysis of her left side, the waves of intense anxiety and panic flowing through her body, the spikes in adrenaline, the tension in her neck, shoulders and back and unexplained neurological symptoms and nerve issues. There were random attacks in the middle of the night where she would wake up choking and unable to breathe. Then there were the feelings of tightness in her throat and chest that started off randomly and soon grew into a symptom every time she tried to eat, and this lasted for several weeks. Then came the brain fog. The massive shift in thinking, confusion, pressure and tingling all throughout her head. Anna would feel the pressure in her head and then it felt like she was falling. Her ability to use her fine motor skills began to be impacted.

Thinking and coming up with the words she was trying to say became a challenge. Her cognitive processing was severely impacted and each morning she woke up not knowing if it was going to be a good day or a bad day. The neurological symptoms were real. The fatigue followed shortly after and was crippling. Anna would wake up in the morning and feel like she had not slept in days. One side of her head would feel heavier than the other and it was as if she was in a constant state of fog and confusion. It was no longer easy to function at work, read through emails, make decisions or process cognitively. It was as if her brain had begun functioning in slow motion, feelings of distortion and inability to comprehend permeated her being. This was so abnormal. The woman she was, slowly began to deteriorate. What was happening...this was not her. She was a Child of God - high-powered business professional, community volunteer, wife, mother, daughter and aunt who was always on point. She was never off her game and now that was all changing so suddenly.

Many joked that Anna could multi-task within an inch of her life. She was a mom who took this role to the extreme...always volunteering, signing up to participate on boards and making sure the kids were academically sound and doing well. She was newly married and trying to keep up with the demands of being the best wife she knew how to be, run a household, raise teenagers, cook, clean and maintain her full-time job, business and co-run her spouse's business. At work, they called her the "hard drive," because she never forgot anything.

She was always on top of her game, took on the hard assignments and managed a team of many who produced projects that impacted her organization world-wide. She was an overachiever to the max who never skipped a beat. Anna's professional career was unshakeable at this point! She was the recipient of many awards and acknowledgements. Sought after by many and was always given the projects with the highest rate of success or failure...depending on how one looked at it. She was always able to juggle the high- pressure demands and pass with flying colors!

One day, it all changed. Anna was sitting in her office and her world as she knew it changed. Suddenly, she could not move the left side of her body and she began to panic. As the intensity of emotions continued to spread, she felt the tingling and numbness moving through her body. Her heart was racing, palpitations were happening to the extreme and she was unable to catch her breath. Out of nowhere panic set in and set in strongly. It all caught her off guard as she had never experienced anything like this before. Immediately she began to look around to search for answers...what is happening? Why is this happening? More importantly...how do I make it stop?

Anna was scheduled to sit on a panel interview that day and immediately began to try to focus and get herself together. She managed to pull herself together to make it to the interview room and about halfway through the interview she realized she was no longer able to fake the appearance of operating as if all was well. As the panel alternated asking questions to the applicant, she looked down at the notes she was taking and noticed that she began writing duplicate sentences. It was as if her brain had completely gone hay wire. Her co-worker quickly noticed the change in behavior and walked her back to her office. He could tell something was off as she was disoriented and had been slightly off balance. She left the office as quickly as she could and as soon as she got to her car and away from everyone, she felt a sigh of relief. The fear of what others were thinking as they watched her go through this medical crisis was too much for her. She never liked to look like she did not have it together in front of people. She was more of a freak- out in private kind of girl.

Now the next hurdle was getting from where she was in the parking lot to some place to figure out what was happening. She called her spouse, and he talked her through her drive and straight to the nearest urgent care facility. During the ride she recalled feeling disoriented and at one point pulled over as she could not figure out where she was and felt completely confused, which was a huge concern as she had driven this route every day to work for years. At this point, she realized she probably had no business driving, but in a panic, she did not know what else to do. About forty-five minutes later she made it to the urgent care facility and was able to be seen by the doctor onsite.

A series of tests were run immediately to rule out a heart attack, stroke or the onset of either condition. The doctor ordered bloodwork, an MRI, an EKG and conducted a physical assessment. After receiving intravenous fluids and ruling out a stroke or heart attack, Anna quickly began to realize this was going to be an adventure to figure out what was truly happening. Without the results of the other tests, the doctor was stumped and insisted on ordering a stress test after evaluating the stress levels in Anna's life. Anna did not feel stressed, but the doctor's jaw dropped as she answered the questions about what she did for work, what she did at home, what were her family dynamics, her travel schedule and the regular day-to-day activities and erratic sleep schedule. The doctor was confused as to how Anna was even functioning. To Anna, her schedule and lifestyle seemed pretty normal as she had lived this way for quite some time.

This was just the beginning of a long torturous three-year journey from doctor to doctor and hospital to hospital. So, what happened? Where did this fearless, fiery overachieving woman go? It was so scary...no rhyme or reason.

ANNA'S DECLINE & THE MEDICAL NIGHTMARES BEGIN

All of the turmoil of Anna's relationship had manifested in the form of health conditions. The years of toxicity, mental and psychological abuse had taken their toll and had developed into a variety of physical responses in her human body. Her body slowly began to deteriorate. First, it was subtle changes like the absence of menstrual cycles, when there was no medical explanation and then on to extreme bouts of fatigue. Anna started to get sick every few months. Her body just let go and she had been down for the count for a week or two at a time. She had to rest up and then get back up and get to it again until the next episode. This continued for some time until one day the rebound from bouts of sickness did not happen as quickly.

Again, she was at work and out of nowhere her body started to tingle and feel numb. Her heart began racing, her breath slowed, and she felt completely disoriented. There was nothing she could do to stop the domino effect. She was able to make it out of work and to seek medical attention immediately. The result...she was found to be completely exhausted, dehydrated and most likely from stress or a virus. All of the tests were inconclusive to include the MRI, CT scan, blood work and physical observation. The doctors had ruled out a heart attack, stroke and any suspected autoimmune conditions. She was held for several hours, given IV fluids and sent home with orders to take some time off of work and focus on getting rest.

Within a few weeks she was back at work and resumed her normal life activities. Until it happened again about six months later. Right before she had experienced a similar episode, she had begun seeing an energy healer. During that time, she was cautioned that there was something going on with her nerves and there was a medical condition brewing and that what was happening was not a genetic condition. It was such a shock and very confusing, but she knew there was something happening to her and just was not sure what was going on. She was advised to be careful of her choice of words as she may experience some health challenges, so she was very conscientious about her choice of words following her session. Two weeks later she found herself lying again in a hospital bed, some tests and no real answers. Same drill...more IV fluids, rest and a series of tests were scheduled.

Fortunately for Anna, her medical challenges began at the beginning of the pandemic, so she was spared the threat of losing her job, because the world had gone into hibernation. During this time of medical crisis, she was afforded the opportunity to work from home and her appearance or lack of functionality was not as noticeable. Working from home during this time period had its perks, because she found herself needing to take a power nap during lunch to get through the afternoon. She also did not have to endure the hour long one-way commute that she had done for so many years. Working in pajamas also had its benefits. Thankfully, she had enough leave saved up to be able to accommodate the many medical appointments she had to attend during this time.

Anna tried to keep up her sense of self and appearance, but it was getting harder and harder. She had been so used to averaging three hours a day at the gym to keep her body fit and for mental clarity. She was used to being in professional work attire and stylish outfits with heels for evenings out on the town. That all changed very quickly as Anna was struggling just to keep her strength up. Showering, clean clothes and no make-up was how she made it through her days. It was not quite the cover model look, but she was doing the best she could to keep up with her appearance.

She continued to go to the hairdresser to get her highlights done and noticed after each visit the chemicals seemed to send her into a tailspin with brain fog. She did not want to let herself go so she pushed through. She knew how much her husband insisted on her having a certain look so there was a bit of pressure that she felt. Despite her efforts, it did not stop her husband's wandering eye, and as time went on, he appeared to be more and more disgusted by her.

DOWN THE RABBIT HOLE

The doctors began with the usual...blood work, physical examination, MRI and CT scan. There were no major findings that linked to what was happening. This is where things became exploratory.

Primary Care Physician Time...

Anna spent a great deal of time at appointments with her Primary Care Physician and lots of follow-ups on a search for answers. Her primary care doctor assigned to her case ran a series of blood tests and then submitted numerous referrals to specialists. The standard tests were performed to include full blood panels. Anna requested some special testing to include Epstein Barr Virus (EBV) to see if perhaps previous Lyme Disease and Mononucleosis infections could be the culprit. The results for EBV were alarming, but the doctors said they were from previous infections so they did not feel it could be the problem. The doctor requested stress tests and found there to be some expected stress occurring, but not enough to cause the myriad of symptoms occurring.

Her doctor was becoming increasingly frustrated with her as she felt that Anna just needed to rest and relax. One could say that Anna was being treated as if she was making up this whole nightmare and there were no medical issues occurring. With

Anna's frustrations growing, she asked the doctor about environmental causes and pleaded for mold and allergen testing to be performed. With hesitation the doctor put in the orders. In the meantime, Anna had private air quality testing conducted to address possible home factors as a potential cause of her ailments. She had read so much about mold and its harmful health effects.

Chiropractor Time...

It was time to get more creative with her care, so Anna decided to seek the evaluation of an outside chiropractor who introduced holistic practices as part of the treatment plan. She had seen chiropractors for her neck and back and the random onset of neurological symptoms. She traveled to find the top chiropractors in the field, because she knew her case was not the norm, and she wanted the best and brightest on her team. The first chiropractor she worked with was well known and had a lengthy career with some of the top athletes in the country. She knew she was in the right place when she arrived, and he immediately knew where to start. He took the time to listen to her concerns, look through her medical files and went to work developing a protocol to support her body at this phase of her body's struggle.

He went through a process of deduction to include addressing the following questions before beginning...was it an alignment needed, pinched nerves, the vagus nerve or a central nervous system gone haywire issue? She was immediately evaluated for central nervous system challenges and possible vagus nerve issues. The doctor had determined that her central nervous system, both sympathetic and parasympathetic, was running simultaneously with no end in sight. It was as if her fight or flight response was never inactive. Her body was always in a heightened state of alert. She began seeing him upwards of three times a week and would receive adjustments to help alleviate the pressure and tension in her back, neck and muscles throughout her body. She would be treated with an Electrical Nerve Stimulation machine to help loosen the muscles. Stretches were conducted during the sessions to loosen the tension in the body, as her muscles were so tight and no matter what she did, she could not loosen her muscles. A regiment of supplements were prescribed to assist the body with the most critical support needed at the time. The treatments provided relief for the time being.

As time progressed, Anna would go to visit her family and had identified a well-known chiropractor in her hometown who was willing to support her current treatment plan and the direction of her doctor back home. Collaboratively, they performed treatment that supported Anna's physical structure and appropriate supplementation. He oversaw her care when she was traveling and introduced additional options and treatments to support her current plan.

Neurologist Time...

First up was the neurology referral. The neurologists conducted the standard patient evaluations and reviewed all of the scans taken in urgent care. Another MRI was ordered. After completion of all the tests and no real concrete findings, minus a small area of concern, the assigned neurologist eventually asked for a second opinion. That is when all of exploratory testing began again.

The MRI...

Because there were so many neurological symptoms and concerns it was determined that MRIs were needed to do comparative studies from her previous MRIs. The only finding was a small flair on the right front side of her brain, which was perplexing as they thought it was small enough to not be that much of a concern.

The doctors said it may have been a side effect from having Lyme Disease or possibly the onset of Multiple Sclerosis. No way to say for sure unless a spinal tap was conducted. The spinal tap was Anna's last resort as she knew how risky that procedure could be, and she was not up for that approach until all other options had been exhausted.

The EEG...

The neurologist decided it was time to put in the test for an EEG and so Anna scheduled that to be conducted. She arrived for the test and was hooked up to all of the monitors and laid there as the test was performed. It was torture, as the lights kept flashing. She truly had reached neurological exhaustion and was beyond the ability to function once the test was complete. She felt completely disoriented and literally could barely function once the test was complete. Anna got in the elevator, went down a level and looked for the exit to the building. As people spoke to her as she walked by them, she felt completely lost. She could not figure out where the sound was coming from or how to get out of the building. The most interesting part was she was very familiar with the building so the disorientation was wild.

It was determined that one side of her brain was responding slower than the other, but there was nothing definitive as to why. A longer study was set up to further explore what was going on. Another neurologist was requested to look at the case and submitted a series of testing for some very scary and rare autoimmune conditions. Both neurologists on the case collaborated to look into potential neurological explanations for the symptoms being experienced by Anna and both kept running into dead ends. Again, no medical explanation was found. However, one finding that was presented was that the brain waves were moving slower on the right of Anna's brain, but the doctors were not sure why. They recommended medication to subside the tingling and pressure felt in the brain.

Anna was not receptive to this recommendation, because they could not give her a clear explanation as to what was going on and she did not want to take medications unless they could identify the root cause of why she needed them.

Muscle Specialist Time...

With all of the mounting symptoms...the tension in Anna's body continued to increase and now the pain and tension in her neck, shoulders and back were becoming worse. The trips to the chiropractor helped, but the adjustments were not holding for long and what was thought to be a deficiency in nutrients was just triggering more physical body responses. The Primary Care Physician and Neurologists also agreed it was time to go and see specialists focusing on the muscular system. During the visit, Anna was asked a series of questions and a physical exam was performed. It was determined that some of the facial muscle freezing and tension in her upper body was being caused by stress and tension. They even said something about muscular inflammation and freezing, which resulted in more prescriptions. After all evaluations were complete, the doctor provided a diagnosis and treatment plan. A fancy medical terminology was added to her chart that basically said her muscles were tense. The solution...topical cream and muscle relaxers. Well, that did not make much sense. Anna did not have an interest in living off of muscle relaxers and topical cream was not that appealing either.

Pulmonologist & Ear Nose & Throat (ENT) Time...

Soon after the journey had begun, Anna started to experience tightness in her throat randomly and shortness of breath. The Primary Care Physician deemed it be allergy induced asthma...a condition she had never had before. It did not make any sense. She had asthma in her family but had never experienced this herself. The neurologist began to explore Myasthenia Gravis as the culprit, but as suspected...the results came back negative.

The pulmonologist was assigned to the case to further identify the cause for the chest tightness and throat tightening. Because Anna was experiencing frequent breathing issues and asthma-like reactions the specialists all wanted her to be seen for further testing. The explanation for tightness in the chest and restricted airways was confirmed as allergy induced asthma. She was advised to continue with the primary care's recommendation of the three different inhaler prescriptions, a series of steroid treatments and a recommendation for tracking when she was experiencing these breathing issues to narrow down the triggers for her episodes. At this point, she was feeling quite defeated. She had seen so many doctors, so many specialists, traveled everywhere and anywhere and now it just seemed like she was being given a diagnosis just to check the box. Sadly, she was not feeling any better. In fact, she was starting to feel worse. Anna began journaling all of the symptoms and with continued issues the doctor finally agreed to refer her to an ENT.

The next round of specialists included the ENT doctor. After assessing Anna's concerns about her throat tightening and feeling closed, he determined that she must be experiencing some form of swelling in her throat or near her vocal cords. The only way to test this theory was to go into the throat with a camera and see what was going on. The ENT performed a scope test to examine the inside of the throat and the findings revealed that there was substantial swelling at the back of her throat, however it was not the diagnosis he had predicted. The swelling was much higher than initially thought and was not correlating with the vocal cords. It was as if the whole back of her throat was swollen and restricting the flow of air. The first order of business was to decrease the swelling so that Anna would experience some relief and be able to breathe easier. The verdict...gastroesophageal reflux disease (GERD)...a form of acid reflux that can have some serious consequences.

GERD? What the hell? That did not make sense. Anna did not have acid reflux issues, BUT out of nowhere she began waking up in the middle of the night choking. She would be choking and unable to swallow, breathe or move for several seconds. Anna would wake up in a panic unable to move or breath...it was as if she was paralyzed. The response was for her to take some acid reflux medications to alleviate the symptoms and allow for some relief. She took the prescription although she still did not feel confident in this answer.

Sleep Specialist Time...

Because of the concerns about the breathing issues and waking up in the middle of the night choking and unable to move, the Primary Care Physician felt it appropriate to conduct a sleep study. She met with the team, they evaluated Anna's health chart and then she was given an apparatus to take home to conduct an overnight test designed to monitor and track her vitals during sleep. They requested to complete an extended sleep study, but she was not really interested in the overnight in-house testing so being able to take the machine home was a much better option in her current condition. Before bed she attached the monitor, as instructed, and pressed the start button on the handheld monitor. In the morning, she removed the machine and dropped it back off at the doctor's office. Not long after returning the monitor, the test results were issued, and the doctor said the tests came back within range...all looked fine. No further tests were conducted, and she was cleared from their department.

Allergist Time...

Well, the reactions continued...now on so many meds and with so many specialists looking at Anna it just seemed like her body was having reaction after reaction. She would eat and it seemed like her body would have immediate responses ranging from breathing issues, rashes, hives and decline in functionality. The brain fog continued to worsen. Some days she could not figure out if she was coming or going. For this reason, an allergist was called in to rule out allergies as the culprit. The tests concluded that the only areas she was experiencing allergic reactions were in environmental areas such as grass, dust mites and pollens. Nothing out of the ordinary and nothing that a little allergy medication could not cure.

Food Testing Time...

After seeing the allergist, Anna's frustrations increased, because once again, there were no solid answers to what was happening to her. Being very practical and methodical, she felt like she needed answers that made sense and so far, nothing was making sense to her. With the recommendation of an outside doctor, Anna decided to hire an independent medical company to conduct a food test. She scheduled the bloodwork through an in-home testing company to perform and her samples were sent to the labs where they conducted extensive food testing to determine if there were any specific foods or food groups that were triggering some of the body responses Anna was encountering. It was during this time that it was discovered that she was having severe reactions to ginger. This was eye opening, because many of the homemade juices and shakes she had been drinking to heal her body included ginger protocols. One answer that finally made sense to her...so Anna immediately removed ginger from her nutritional intake. That was the only finding.

The Mystery Continues...

Upon completion of the long list of specialists, she was sent back to the primary care doctor and neurology team. With the persistence of symptoms and progression of her health worsening, the doctors decided it was time to go for some more in-depth bloodwork and testing.

The only other solution they could think of was some of the rarer disorders or autoimmune conditions. The result...the autoimmune tests...MS.... myasthenia gravis ...lupus and more. Anna grew increasingly fearful as all of the chaos and mayhem surrounding this experimental health adventure had created so much doubt and fear in her mind. She was literally scared out of her mind with all of the potential options they were throwing at her. She followed through with all of the blood testing and surprisingly, all of the tests came back negative. At this point, the doctors had nothing left to offer her. They were completely stumped and were not sure what to do. The only option left that Anna had not tried was the spinal tap. She had purposely held off on the spinal tap, because she knew the risks and did not really want to venture down that path unless it was the absolute last resort. The fear around this test plagued her for months. She was willing to do everything, but the spinal tap, and when all of the options had been exhausted, the last option was to submit to the test that should provide all the answers.

The Spinal Tap...

The last resort...Anna gave in to the neurologist's last option ...the spinal tap. She was fearful and beyond comprehension with concern for the procedure. She scheduled it as a final attempt for answers. She went for the procedure and anxiously awaited the results. As she followed all instructions and laid there in the bed for the recovery time identified by the doctors for the puncture wound to heal in her spine, she quickly realized she was not getting better. The spinal headaches had begun, and the symptoms were worsening. She landed back in the hospital and the doctors were exploring a technique called a "blood patch," which she was not interested in at all. She could not stand up or move without extreme pain as the spinal fluid continued to leak throughout her body, but she also knew she could not risk the doctors going back into her spine. She opted not to proceed with the procedure, go home and rest for several weeks to see if it would resolve on its own. A very risky approach, but she could not bear the thought of anymore torment.

Several weeks later she slowly regained her ability to sit in an upright position without excruciating pain and began to move around with less and less head pain. It was a long recovery process, but she eventually made it through. The most unnerving part of the whole process...the results that ran every possible genetic and autoimmune condition showed that the results were normal. What??? She could barely move. Anna had experienced all of the possible side effects that could happen and there were no profound answers! What the hell will happen next?

Something was still very wrong and there were absolutely NO answers in sight! The thought of any more exploratory medical procedures to her already fragile body was too much for her mind to comprehend. When the results finally came in there were still no explanations for what was happening to Anna. The best anyone could do was point to maybe some lingering effects of Lyme disease she had experienced as a kid. Which by the way...she had to kick and scream to ask to have her Epstein-Barr Virus levels checked and although they were off the charts, they were dismissed as old infections.

Feeling beyond defeated, her husband looked at her and basically said..." see nothing is wrong you are fine." After hearing and not accepting his response, she decided to explore the non- traditional options and seriously consider working with the energy healer as modern medicine had no answers for her.

Therapist Time...

At this point, Anna had gone through just about every medical department, introduced non-traditional approaches and approximately two years in, she still did not have any solid conclusive answers to what had happened and was happening.

She just had a medicine cabinet full of prescriptions and a rolodex of new medical contacts. Anna truly felt like she was a med student going through all of the medical departments to determine what she wanted to specialize in. She was starting to feel like she should be awarded an honorary medical degree! It was crazy.

Because the brain fog and feeling of disorientation persisted, Anna was not surprised when the next stop was to see a therapist to rule out mental health concerns. After seeing two different therapists, because she wanted to get a second opinion, it was determined, by both, that her mental faculties were intact and that anyone who had gone through this many unnerving experiences was within their right to be experiencing the anxiety, panic and frazzled responses that Anna was providing in her sessions. She completed a questionnaire and verbal tests evaluating depression, suicidal ideology, personality disorders and more.

The verdict...no further treatment or appointments required, unless Anna felt she wanted to have sessions to discuss all of the frustrations and stress this was all causing. She was offered to join a woman's support group for women experiencing a great deal of stress and pressure in their lives. She also was prescribed some antihistamines to assist with decreasing the level of anxiety she was experiencing from all of the three-ring circus experiences she continued to go through on her medical journey. She did give them a go and they did not prove helpful in soothing or subsiding some of the symptoms, so she resorted to more natural approaches, such as lemon balm tinctures and lemon balm teas.

Eye Doctor Time...

Then, the vision issues began. It was as if Anna's eyesight was diminishing and then the eye nerve would pulse for hours on end. On to the eye doctor...why not? She had been everywhere else! During this visit, the eye doctor concluded that her vision was fine, with the exception of having bumps under her eyelids that were thought to have developed as a result of years of wearing contact lenses. She prescribed some eye drops to heal the bumps and changed her lens to daily wear versus extended wear.

HER SOUL WAS CRYING OUT...

It was at this point in her journey, Anna realized that her body had finally had enough. All of the years of running her physical form to the max, lack of self-care, emotional and physical abuse had all brought her to this moment. Through all of these experiences her body began to bottle up and create heavy negative energies trapped like bubbles inside her being. Her soul had finally had enough! It said...no more...not today...not another day! Because she was so stubborn and head strong, she continued to push through her human experience blindly and just became consumed by the madness that was happening to her physical body.

She kept searching for solutions, only to find that there were no logical medical explanations or answers that would shed light on what she was truly experiencing. It was at that moment that her brain finally got the message. Her soul was crying out for help! Her soul had finally had enough. No more pain, no more pushing her body to the max, no more abuse...it stops now...not another year. She was not listening to what was happening, was not listening to her intuition and was not being true to herself.

Anna had lost herself in a life that was not hers, a life that stripped every ounce of who her true soul was and every sense of dignity away from her. No more...God finally had enough and since she was not getting the message, it was time for a wakeup call and that is exactly what this moment in time turned out to be. Her soul could no longer lie dormant. It was time...time to awaken her true self and true purpose. No longer did she get to call the shots. Her soul was on this Earth for a purpose and being hidden away and not fulfilling her mission could no longer go unnoticed. It was time for some divine intervention and that is just what she experienced. Once she was willing to accept that this was bigger than her and she could not save herself...she needed someone bigger and stronger...she called on God to walk her through this hell she had been living, because she knew she just could not take it anymore.

EXPLORING THE NON-TRADITIONAL

Anna knew in her heart that she had exhausted all of the traditional options available to her. She had seen every doctor in the various specialties, and her Primary Care Physician and Neurologists were beyond frustrated with her. They told her time and rest would be the best recovery for whatever had happened to cause her entire being to go haywire. They assured her it would resolve itself with time. She could not accept this answer as nothing had been solved and her symptoms would subside and return, and new ones would surface unexpectedly. It was like she was left alone in the dark to figure it out and she was not quite sure what to do next.

Throughout this time, she began educating herself on anything and everything that was related to what she was going through. This was when she began incorporating all of the YouTube videos, TedTalks, WebMD, medical journals and an extensive book list of reading began. Anna spanned in range from books and teachings from Joyce Meyer, Dr. Joe Dispenza, Deepak Chopra, Donna Eden, Sarah Jakes Roberts, Esther Hicks and Jerry Hicks, Eckhart Tolle, Gary Zukav, Michael Singer, Dr. Caroline Leaf, Anthony William, Tony Robbins, Dr. Ramani Durvasula, Oprah Winfrey, Lisa Bilyeu, Jamie Kern Lima, Gary Chapman, Shawn Stevenson, David Deida, Rainie Howard and so many more. She studied the teachings of each and was able to learn and take away valuable information and lessons.

Anna began going to seminars to immerse herself in the experiences to see if that would create a mental shift to assist her with creating an armor of emotional toughness as she began to realize she was going to have to heal herself. She purchased program after program to see which ones would resonate. As Anna continued to discover and educate herself about the neurological functions, nerves and the quantum field she fumbled upon Annie Hopper's Dynamic Neural Retraining System (DNRS). DNRS was a program that was designed to retrain the limbic system in the brain using the concept of neuroplasticity. Once again, Anna and her mom decided to jump all in and get the program and get to work. During the course of several weeks, Anna and her mom studied the program and followed the exercises to begin the process of retraining her brain. This was another resource and tool that truly helped as she continued to fight the medically un-addressed neurological symptoms. During and throughout the program, Anna began to find herself reconnecting with pleasant memories that allowed her to start creating healthier neuro connections in her brain. She basically was re-wiring her brain functions to assist with pushing through the intense moments of fear and anxiety that plagued her every time she left the house. Her mind had been constantly burdened with ruminating thoughts of not being able to make it through the drive to the grocery store or what would happen if she had a moment in the store. The DNRS gave her actionable items to mentally perform and re- hearse in times of stress.

As Anna continued her healing journey with the Medical Medium protocols, she stumbled across Dr. Bradley Nelson's book, *Emotion Code* ®. This was another powerful tool on her journey. Emotion Code ® is a program and series of tools, using a form of questions and muscle testing, which was designed to identify trapped emotions in the body and release them. Anna stumbled across an upcoming live seminar and quickly signed up. She listened, learned and participated fully in the seminar. She was fortunate to get called upon by Dr. Bradley, and he demonstrated the technique on her.

She identified a source of discomfort, and he began performing the technique and upon completion of the technique she instantly felt less tension and relief in her neck. Once completed, she actually signed up to take the certification program in the methodologies and teachings of Emotion Code ®. During her studies of the program, she was required to perform the technique on others with the oversight of a mentor. She performed and documented her experiences of over twenty subjects. This was an opportunity for Anna to find immediate relief and she was able to perform it on herself as well.

Another helpful program she came across in her quest for knowledge was Dr. Caroline Leaf's book, *Cleaning Up Your Mental Mess*. Upon completion of reading the book and understanding her philosophies, she downloaded Dr. Leaf's Neurocycle App that assisted in monitoring, tracking and resetting your neuro responses and cycles when certain events or triggers occurred. She found her teachings to be particularly helpful when identifying unhealthy patterns, triggers and trauma responses.

It was as if each program, and the research she explored, provided one more tool to put in her toolbox and aided her for each step of her journey. Along this very windy path, she would adopt the strategies that worked for the time being and discard the ones that did not resonate with her.

The Energy Healer...

Anna and Lionel had met with a very notorious energy healer, Stacey, prior to Anna's health decline. It was during that session that some concerns were revealed about communication in their relationship. During that conversation, the healer had mentioned some energy blockages for both of them surrounding their childhood experiences. Lionel was dismissive of these findings and Anna had followed up with the healer to get further insight as to what was being referenced about herself. Shortly after the couple session, she met with Stacey again for an energy clearing session. It was during this time that Stacey picked up on some health concerns involving her nerves. She cautioned Anna about several concerns and mentioned to be careful about using certain terms and phrases. It was apparent that Stacey saw the looming health challenges that were being shared in this section.

Having had prior experience working with Stacey, once the health madness began, Anna sought her out to have her perform energy work focused specifically on her health. She went for sessions twice a week initially and later began to work her way down to once a week. With the help of energy work she was able to regain feeling and restore some of the usage of her left side. The headaches and brain fog started to subside, and it was necessary to go for sessions weekly to keep progress moving forward. As improvements started to happen there seemed to be something that was still off. She would feel well when she left the sessions and a few days later things would go back to the way they had been. Stacey would ask what she had done between sessions...food she ate...exercise routine...work routine...rest, etc. Anna would share her medical results, tests that were scheduled and upcoming and collaborated to identify other areas and potential medical diagnosis to explore.

As the tests kept coming back with no medical findings...the stress levels, chakra imbalances and chaos being experienced at home were thought to be the culprit. The lack of support and the feeling of the "unknown" was complicating matters further. She continued the sessions for several months and began exploring some more lifestyle-related causes for what was going on. She explored heavy metals in the body, air quality, environmental pollutants, physical and emotional stress from her strained marriage. The healer had picked up on the dysfunction and chaos at home and noticed that Anna's spouse did not have much empathy for what she had been experiencing.

As a matter of fact, she began picking up on the toxicity that was causing an unhealthy environment for her to heal. Still, with the assistance of the healer, Anna explored some of the more feasible solutions that she thought she could address. She had air quality tests run in the home, installed air purifiers and air machines throughout the home.

The energy sessions were helpful and assisted in uncovering some energy blocks and the discovery of limiting beliefs that she had adopted over time. It was a very practical natural solution to her physical ailments that were not being solved by her traditional medical professionals. She learned about breathwork. The neurological symptoms were persistent, and the sessions offered some relief with the manual manipulation and movement of energy. Anna learned about solutions such as peppermint oil for severe headaches and mustard seed baths for detoxing environmental toxins out of the body. The tools she was learning were much more practical solutions for long-term self-care.

The Connection...

Several sessions in, the healer connected Anna with Lisa. Lisa was a client that Stacey had worked with who had a background in neuroscience and had experienced autoimmune condition challenges herself. Lisa had recently moved from the area, but still kept in touch with her friends back home and was more than willing to share her knowledge and experiences with Anna. She was beyond knowledgeable in autoimmune and health altering experiences. Lisa was kind, patient and completely understood the emotions that Anna was feeling throughout the mystery illness process. She was a saving grace and made herself available anytime Anna had questions or needed support with the various protocols that she shared and introduced to Anna. Lisa introduced Anna to the Medical Medium lifestyle and protocols and all things celery and organic.

The Medical Medium Protocols...

This was a pivotal moment in Anna's healing journey! She started with ordering the Medical Medium books, *Cleanse to Heal, Liver Rescue, Celery Juice, Thyroid Healing and Life Changing Foods.*" Anna's mother also purchased the books to learn right alongside her and participated in all of the protocols as well like a true team player! They began watching the live videos on Facebook and YouTube and tried to soak up all of the knowledge they could find.

She thought if the doctors could not identify the cause, it was time for her to take matters into her own hands and to explore mystery symptoms and holistic solutions. It was during this time that Anna began to experience some relief from the environmental and emotional toxins she was being exposed to. She saw some inflammation in her body decrease, but although she was seeing progress, there was still something that was not quite clicking. The brain fog was improving but was not fully dissipating. Each day was like a game of Russian Roulette. She might be on point or might be foggy. It was a surprise for her and everyone around her each day. She followed these protocols faithfully for approximately a year and a half and began to see some improvements, but still suffered from the brain fog and neurological challenges.

Anna did not hesitate to begin all prescribed protocols based on the books and guidance recommended to her. She began learning about supplements, juicing, heavy metal detoxing, daily lemon water and celery juice and so much more. She eliminated eggs and dairy and went to a low-fat intake diet to begin warding off the high levels of EBV in her body. Anna had promptly gone back to her doctors and asked to have her EBV levels re- tested after learning about EBV being the culprit for so many of her symptoms. Her doctors were reluctant to perform the tests, but once they did, they found that her counts were well over 700 and again responded by saying that was from past infections and not to worry. Anna had been educating herself and knew that she was not okay with that answer, so she decided to take it a step further and begin completing the 3-6-9 Advanced cleanse protocols. She was determined to ward off the culprits and do whatever was necessary to begin cleaning up her body.

For two solid years, Anna continued following all protocols. She would start every morning with Medical Medium's morning cleanse, which consisted of thirty-two ounces of lemon water, followed by thirty-two ounces of freshly made celery juice and then a heavy metal detox smoothie. The ingredients of the smoothie were very filling with a substantial number of wild blueberries so that often became her breakfast. The remainder of her meals were filled with fresh fruits and vegetables and supported by lots of herbs and leafy greens. She began learning the power of lemon balm, cat's claw, licorice root and L-Lysine to combat many of her symptoms. Zinc was a game changer for her. She would take it each morning with the protocols she was following. When she felt an illness or cold coming on, she would follow the Zinc-Shock therapy and/or the Vitamin-C shock therapy. There were more times than not that she would find herself flipping through the back section of *Cleanse to Heal* looking up the protocols for various symptoms and identifying which approach to take to tackle the concerns at that time. She became well versed in juicers and had finally settled on one she preferred after going through several others. She had researched supplement companies and had selected an organic based supplement company as her go to for all of her supplement needs. Each night was concluded with a lemon balm tea. When she knew, she was going to experience higher stress situations she would prepare by reaching out to Lisa for extra guidance and support. She quickly learned that L-Lysine was her best friend during times of stress. Lisa began teaching her about neurological functions and cutting-edge research to help point

Anna in the right direction for further research and to share knowledge.

Anna even created a YouTube channel devoted to sharing information and helping others heal from symptoms that ailed them based on all that she had been learning on her journey. She found herself answering so many questions when she had been shopping in the stores for her ingredients for her juices and detox recipes that it was just as easy to create a channel and pass out cards when people began asking questions. Anna knew she had to become the CEO of her own health if she ever wanted to get to the bottom of all of this chaos!

Continuing the Search for Knowledge...

Anna stumbled across many social media influencers and key players in the health industry and started learning everything she could about organically eating, clean eating, the importance of sleep and self-care. She came across Shawn Stevenson's *Eat Smarter* and *Sleep Smarter* books and programs. She read through all of the books and began sharing the information with her friends and family.

During this time, she continued on with her weekly sessions with the energy healer and continued to take two steps forward and two steps back. It was as if she would make strides towards feeling better and then another setback would happen. It was at this point in the journey of exploring all possible medical diagnosis and health-related possibilities that the healer began exploring less obvious explanations. It was during this time that limiting beliefs, traumas and abusive relationships were exposed and slowly the peeling of the onion began to occur. Anna was not prepared for what was uncovered, but she began to see that this was all part of the process and the journey of healing that had to occur. This is where authenticity and TRUTH begin.

She began learning about meditation and breathwork. This was a totally new experience for Anna, so she began with guided meditations to begin the process and learn. Anna also joined a live meditation group that meant monthly with the energy healer. This was her first experience in the transcendental world. Prior to following Dr. Joe Dispenza, and Esther Hicks and Jerry Hicks, she had not comprehended the 3-D, 4-D and 5-D worlds. This was her introduction to worlds beyond physical form. As she continued to grow in her knowledge and understanding of the Spiritual world, she began to question so many things that she had learned throughout her life. How much of what she had learned and experienced was even real? It was mind boggling. She felt like an infant waking up and learning how to live all over again.

Anna began journaling as well. She found that writing down her happenings, the symptoms, her thoughts and feelings and any other things that came to mind assisted her with tracking her progress. This also assisted her in identifying which things were working and which ones were not as helpful. She was able to glean a lot of insight through her writings. During times when setbacks would surface, she would pull out her journal to remind her just how far she had come. Anna even joined a woman's group focused on building esteem and exploring limiting beliefs and re-defining perception of self. After going through this roller coaster ride of health issues, and the mounting psychological and emotional abuse in her relationship, it had taken its toll on her ability to believe in herself and who she thought she was all these years. Calling in the support of this group during this very transformational time added additional teachings and skills and provided resources and frameworks that assisted her in creating a new refined and stronger Anna.

Holistic Healing Modalities...

At her annual eye check-up, Anna shared what had been happening to her. She expressed her frustrations, fears and the lack of clarity with what continued to transpire with her health. During the visit she showed the eye doctor the various eye nerve twitches that had begun, and the constant vision changes she was experiencing. The pressure behind her eyes, her pupils changing constantly and then the feeling of diminishing site on and off at no uncertain time. The eye doctor conducted an exam and found her eyes to be intact. No structural concerns and no visual explanation. It was at this time that she provided Anna with a referral to a holistic wellness center.

At this point in her journey, Anna was on a quest to live the healthiest, longest and most fulfilling life she possible could dream of...it took her health completely falling apart to get her here, but better late than never! She had been suffering for so long and knew that if there was even a small chance that this was a solution to her struggles, she would put all of her effort into it. Little did she know that this was going to be a true game changer. This elevated her spiritual awakening and healing to a new level.

Anna picked up the phone, made the call and scheduled her first appointment. The appointment was set for a month out, as that was the first available. She was able to schedule with another practitioner, as the one that was recommended to her was booked several months out. Anna was not familiar with holistic healing methods but had heard many great success stories from others who chose the non-traditional path to healing. She had been familiar with some of the natural remedies that had been used over the years such as Olbas oil on the chest for congestion, fresh squeezed oranges and honey in tea for colds and so many others. She was not clear on how it all worked and the protocols. Anna had a good feeling about this path though she felt that she had nothing to lose, and she was going to give it a shot.

THE INTRODUCTION OF THE HOLISTIC APPROACH...

The wait was over, Anna had arrived at the wellness facility and as she walked in the door she was met with the fresh scent of essential oils. She immediately felt a sense of relief and calm wash over her body. As she glanced around, she noticed the Cross in the corner of the room and heard the sound of music spreading God's messages through the speakers. The woman behind the counter greeted her with a warm smile and provided her with paperwork to complete for her appointment. She offered Anna some water and asked if there was anything else she could get her. As Anna looked around the room, she saw so many new things, there were several stands in the lobby that had everything from essential oils, all natural bath products, crystals, supplements and so many other holistic products. The atmosphere was so warm and welcoming. She felt a wave of peace entering her body.

As Anna sat alone in the office waiting room for her appointment so many things crossed her mind. She had been to so many doctors, run so many tests, was a human experiment and still no answers prevailed. She sat there waiting and waiting ...wondering...would this be the appointment that provided some clarity...some answers? She felt like this was her last option...last resort. So many trips, so many tests and yet no answers. It was frustrating, confusing and slowly the light started to dim. She did not want to give up...she did not want to stop fighting...the only thing she could cling to in this state of desperation was her Faith. Faith that GOD would see her through, that she had been led to the right place, that this would be the chance to start her healing journey.

Anna sat in the chair fiddling with her phone and jotting down some notes for her appointment, the feeling of anxiousness continued to creep in, making it seem like the clock was standing still. So much was riding on this appointment. She took slow deep breaths to calm and quiet her mind as she felt the thoughts racing through her head. If she could just hang in there long enough to get to the room for her appointment everything would be okay. She just knew it...she felt it! She was not sure how or why, but she began to trust the feeling in the pit of her stomach that clearly said that she was in the right place, and this is where she would find her answers.

As her name was called, she froze...looked up, swallowed back the tears and felt mixed emotions of fear and relief. She had no idea what to expect but it was time. Time to move...time to learn...time to be open to a new way of thinking and approaching her health journey. She sat down and Nathan smiled and made some small talk. She felt anxiety and panic flooding over her body and was trying to act normal. He could see the distress in her face and continued to explain the scan, what it does and how it works. Nathan was a kindhearted man who was genuinely concerned about what had brought Anna to the office. He assured her that she was in the right place, and this was the line of business they were in...addressing the many medical mysteries that modern medicine continuously dismisses. As she described her symptoms and issues, he seemed familiar with all of them and had very sound and logical explanations for what she had been going through. She had learned more during that scan than she had in two years sitting through all of the doctor's appointments she had gone through.

About an hour and a half later she was handed a report that provided a comprehensive overview of all of her organ function levels, emotions, meridians and all of the toxins, viruses, metals and more that she had been exposed to and that were disrupting the functionality of her body. This report provided a

RE-CREATION Page | 42

baseline of biomarkers that would set the tone for the holistic natural approach to her care and healing journey for her body. As Nathan continued to explain what all of the feedback from the scan meant, she felt a sense of calm and serenity flood over her body. Finally...someone who heard what she was saying, listened and was able to logically understand and explain what was happening to her physical being. She was not crazy...she had not imagined the symptoms...there was proof sitting before her that clearly explained what was going on inside her body and why things were happening the way they were.

Upon completion of their discussion, he provided a list of protocols to be taken that would begin a new healing journey... a journey that would take time but would be worth every moment of effort put into it. The starting place would be restoring Anna's central nervous system. It had totally taken a hit and was in desperate need of repair and he knew just what to do to begin the process. Nathan was very frank with Anna and let her know that this would be a process and not an overnight fix. Anna was fine with that, she had already spent the last two years working towards restoring her health, so as long as he was confident, she was fixable, she was willing to put in the work. Nathan gave her a plan that involved a combination of supplements, spiritual homework, breathwork and some soul searching. He gathered all of the supplements she would be taking over the course of the next four – six weeks and documented how much of each would be taken so that she had a clear concise plan to follow. He made it as simple as possible for her so that she did not feel too overwhelmed as he completely understood that her neurological symptoms were not in sync, and she was having difficulty comprehending and digesting all of the new information she had just received.

That day she walked out of the office not really sure what had happened, but she knew something profound was underway. She was listened to, heard and understood. This alone was a completely different experience than what she had been going through the past year and half. No one looked at her like she was crazy or treated her like she had lost her mind. The level of dignity and respect she had received made it clear that she was in the right place. As she was handed her protocol listing and her reports, she made her way to the counter to collect her supplements and was on her way. She left the office with a totally different outlook and new lease on life! She was feeling a sense of knowing that she was where she was supposed to be and on the right path. Fear and uncertainty began to diminish, and she began to let her guard down and trust that God was walking alongside her as she embarked upon what presented as a health journey, but very quickly became a mind, body and spirit journey.

She went home and began to read over all of the information that was provided to her. Anna scanned through the entire report, positive and negative food lists, emotion chart and her protocol listing. The protocols called for a series of supplements set to detoxify her body and organs from the viruses, allergens, chemicals, man-made toxins and more that were polluting her central nervous system. The scans conducted during her appointment revealed toxic overload to a very high magnitude to include heavy metals, chemicals, vaccines and so many other concerns. Given the state of Anna's health, it was determined that the treatment protocols would be geared towards the most urgent area of concern. The journey would be a long one, but she was assured that it would be worth it in the end. She did not completely understand everything, but it sounded very logical and sound. She was willing to give it her best shot and trust that God had led her here to find answers and heal her mind, body and soul.

VISIT NUMBER TWO...

Her follow-up appointment rolled around several weeks later and it was time for a follow-up scan to track her progress. What a blessing...her body was responding to the protocols, and she was beginning to experience relief. Her biomarkers had decreased, and her body was receptive to the protocols she had been following. During this visit, she learned so many more things about herself, her body's responses and the protocols that she had been using. She explored positive and negative food reactions in her body. Explored meditation techniques, calming techniques and ways to ground herself when feeling overstimulated and overanxious. Areas such as self-care, sleep routine and prioritizing self were discussed. Nathan also began educating her on the healing benefits of crystals. It was during this session that the chaos of her life came up during discussion and she began to open up and acknowledge the emotional and mental toxicity that was happening at home. This unhealthy environment was contributing to her inability to heal in a healthy safe environment.

As the session concluded, she gathered her notebook full of notes she had taken throughout their discussion and thanked him for his continued support of her healing. Anna left with so much knowledge and so much more to explore as she continued to explore the Spiritual world from a lens she had not previously understood. She was in awe of all that she was learning, but even more so at the progress she was starting to make in such a short period of time. It was absolutely inspiring to know that there was a renewed sense of hope. She quickly realized that this was exactly where she was supposed to be, and the true healing was already underway. This was not going to be a quick fix, but a journey that was going to require a tremendous amount of work on Anna's part. The missing puzzle piece had been located and the souls she was surrounded by were sent by

God to walk with her on the next phase of her journey and serve as guides.

As Anna continued to benefit from the relief resulting from the protocols, she unexpectedly contracted COVID. This was a minor setback as the virus had compromised her system and had created some unanticipated challenges. Contracting the virus had altered the initial course of the treatment protocols. Nathan performed a scan was empathetic and very focused on ensuring that the next phase of treatment would be able to clear up the remnants of the virus. Anna was immediately treated for her symptoms with a salt booth, sauna, electromagnetic mat and a supplement regiment that would lessen the impact of the virus. She was thankful and appreciative for his quick response to her concerns, as this was still during the height of the pandemic, and many were fearful of interacting or engaging with anyone who had been diagnosed with the virus. Again, she was treated with dignity and respect and treated with the utmost care and love.

VISIT NUMBER THREE...

It was now time for Anna's third follow-up appointment and this time she would be seeing a woman, Linda, who she was initially referred to by her eye doctor. She was well-known and Anna was excited to finally meet her for the first time. She arrived on time for her appointment and patiently waited to hear her name called. The wait was longer than she expected, but she had learned from her previous visits that this is part of the process. Patience is a virtue and not one that Anna was particularly skilled at in any area of her life. As she fiddled and felt the anxious, panicky feelings come over her body, she feared not being able to sit any longer. Her body would randomly go into a frenzy without warning. The episodes were decreasing since she began her treatments, but every once in a while, she was caught off guard by the intensity of the feelings. It was like her whole body was tingling everywhere and the fight or flight feelings were intensifying.

She tried to focus...put on some music on her phone...began reading a book...all in an effort to look busy, productive and less awkward. It felt like the time was standing still. Eventually, she heard her name and could not have jumped up any faster to get back to Linda's office, who was known in the area as the healer of all mysterious and serious conditions. As she walked into the room, she felt a sigh of relief rush over her.

Nathan had already conducted the scan and now it was time for Linda to come in to review the scan and discuss the protocols. It was not very long before Linda could see the distress on Anna's face. She took one look at Anna and realized there was a little more than what met the eye. There were so many things going on that were causing a complete overload to the central nervous system and her neurological functions. Inflammation, toxins and energetic imbalances had ravaged her body. The list was long and the protocols to deconstruct and reconstruct the central nervous system and cellular functions were going to take time. Building upon the standard protocols that Nathan had prescribed to Anna and the lingering remnants of COVID, Linda tweaked the plan a bit. Linda also began to explain that Anna would have to be willing to do the work...the inner work...that was going to be required to really heal her soul. The work that no amount of supplementation could fix. She had to "sit with herself." Anna was not quite sure what she agreed to, but it was an unequivocal YES...she was willing to do whatever needed to be done to restore her health!

The scans revealed some expected and some very unexpected results. Common exposure to household cleaners, toxins and pollutants from daily life and residual effects from virus were all present. Some were present in previous scans, and some were newer. No surprise, as these findings were being addressed since her first visit and progress was being made, but because of the overload it would take several rounds of protocols and time to cleanse her body. What was not expected was the poison findings that Anna could not have easily been exposed to. This was a clear indicator of foul play and complete attack on the already delicate central nervous system. Immediately, protocols were put in place to detox the body and begin the reparation process of the effects. Because there was so much damage and so many areas to restore, the process was not as easy as a "one-size fits all." Ensuring that the most critical areas were addressed first, Linda went right to work and devised a methodical approach to restoring her health in a very sequential way.

As Anna did in previous visits, she jotted down notes and asked the questions she had written down prior to her appointment. She was so curious about the process and all of the information that she was learning about the human body's inner workings. For the first time, she realized the complexity of the human body. Yet, day in and day out, people get up and go and just expect everything to work. Anna gathered her reports, discussed her progress and made her way to the checkout area to collect supplements and schedule her next appointment. In some what of shock and awe, she departed the office and realized she had a lot to think about on her ride home.

Once she got in the car, she exhaled and decided it was time to really make some decisions. It was on that ride home that she realized that she had so much more to face on her journey to restoring her human functions. She had so many questions...so many concerns...so many unknowns. Her body had been fighting a war and it was not going to be a speedy healing process. She first had to acknowledge and accept that she had literally been battling a near death experience and that put some things into perspective for her. She could not believe that during this time of test after test and illness after illness the unsuspected was occurring as well. This was a lot to process. She stared at those results in disbelief and vowed at that moment that she was going to heal come hell or high water. She had come too far, and she had her children relying on their mother. She was madly in love with the man she had married and had to face the fact that she was living in a delusion...one where her love was so deep and so real, and the reciprocation of such depth was not possible from the other end...not even a fraction of her love for him. The level of toxicity, both intentional and unintentional, that this relationship had inflicted upon her human body was more than her soul could bear. Her soul was giving her all of the signs and she chose to ignore red flag after red flag to continue this fairytale she had dreamed of playing out since she was a young girl.

Now things were different though...this experience she was re-creating was costing Anna her health, sanity, morals, values and had deeply affected her children's and family's lives as well. This no longer was a safe space for the love she was so freely giving. It became a moment in time where she had to make a decision...a decision to put herself first and the lives of her children first. A time where she had to choose HER...a moment to realize that self-love was the only thing that could save her at this stage of her life. She was not ready to say goodbye to her human experience, she was here to see her children grow and was determined to do so. Not sure what to do, she looked to the sky with tears in her eyes and called on God to give her strength to walk through this fire. With sadness and disbelief in her heart she pulled up her big girl pants, thanked God for keeping her on Earth and thanked the woman who would become the key to solving so many of her medical mysteries. It was at this moment the next phase of Anna's journey had begun.

The follow-up appointments would be her new norm as she knew she was going to be working with Linda and Nathan for quite a while, as there was work to be done physically and spiritually. Anna began to incorporate some other modalities to include foot detox baths, mat treatments, sauna sessions, salt booth treatments and energy sessions with tuning forks, sound bowls and binaural beats. The combination of treatments was designed to assist the body and mind with the healing process.

SHE'S AWAKENING

This was the start of not only a physical health healing journey, BUT it was the beginning of her Awakening! No longer could she remain blind to what was really going on. No longer could she allow herself to accept lies, deceit, infidelity, mistreatment and psychological abuse. Her mother's words echoed in her ears "why do you want my life?" She never understood those words and then it became abundantly clear that Anna had RE-CREATED her mother's life. Of course, there was a plot twist, as no one had suspected the unexpected was happening to her. In that moment, she had to make some decisions...some really tough decisions. With that, she chose herself...she chose to say goodbye to the lies...the deceit...the betrayal and walk the path with God to salvation where she would have the opportunity to re- create who she wanted to be, live her life and raise her children in peace, while she continued to reconstruct her body's most precious functions and vital systems with the help of a Linda and Nathan who had been blessed with the gift of healing so many!

She knew if she wanted to stay alive and to heal, she had to end her marriage and sadly she was not ready to...she still had hope. Hope that this all was not true, that this could be fixed, that this was all just a misunderstanding. Then reality sunk in, and she realized he did not love her, he did not love her children...he just loved the benefits of what he received from the relationship. As Anna continued her protocol treatments, she slowly began to build up her strength and her thoughts became clearer and clearer. She was in a better place to make sound logical decisions now that she was regaining her health and strength. Prior to now she was in a daze, almost like a fog that kept her from being able to think clearly. She was too busy always being in survival mode with her fight or flight response constantly activated.

Every morning, afternoon and night she would grab her protocol listing, shot glass, supplements and her Faith and begin to go down the list. She stopped questioning the process and decided it was time...time to "trust the process". Because at this point, she had exhausted all of her options and she had been brought to her knees and when she looked around...she realized that the only one who could save her at this point was God and herself. She called on Him and asked for His mercy...asked for His help...and decided that surrender was the only way to walk this journey. She slowly began to release the reigns and loosen control of the expected outcomes she had always carefully and methodically thought out every time she approached anything she did. It was time, time to get in the passenger seat and let God do the navigating. She was determined, dedicated and ready to do the work. As Anna continued to follow the plan provided to her, she began tracking her daily activity, functions, self-care activities, fluid intake and physical exercise. She would prepare tracking reports and submitted them to the wellness team as part of gauging her improvements. In the reports, she would highlight areas of concern and/or questions that arose throughout the process. There were several weeks where she felt unnerved. Her body was quite resistant at the beginning. It was such a challenge to embrace patience, surrender and just breathe. Her body was so far out of alignment that she experienced regular feelings of floating, tingling, balance issues and sensations of anxiousness, sporadically.

As supplementation began to work its magic and the body began eliminating toxins there were some expected resistance responses. She would reach out to Linda to inquire and do a sanity check on the feelings and challenges arising. This was when she began to learn that this was normal and homeopathic crisis is a real thing when the body becomes accustomed to existing in a polluted environment.

There were some challenging moments where she had to sit back and learn breathing techniques, meditation and grounding. This was all so very new to her. Sitting still...not the norm. Breathing, well that was always in short supply in her world and grounding ...what the hell is that?

GOING A STEP FURTHER

As Anna began to feel stronger and stronger, day by day, month by month, she decided to commit to re-creating a better, stronger, wiser Anna. There was no way, after what she had been through, she was going to throw in the towel. She knew her journey with her spiritual and wellness guides was just getting started! She felt like there was so much to do and so much to learn and she wanted to do it as quickly as possible. For the first time in Anna's life, she made a decision to stop abusing her mind, body and soul and start loving, nourishing and appreciating the human body that God so carefully designed for her. She realized that she had taken her body for granted and that a tall cup of gratitude was in order!

The scans and supplement protocols were just the beginning. There was so much more to explore. Anna knew she had a body, but it is like buying a car. You get the car, do the basic maintenance and oil changes and expect it to keep running, but what about preventative maintenance? What about long-term maintenance? No one ever really sits down and teaches you everything you need to know about this human vessel in which your soul resides. Okay...maybe a few people on the Earth study this and understand it, but the vast majority do not...they just expect to be able to get up and go. So now Anna was on a quest...a thirst for knowledge...to ensure that her body was in tip top shape and functioning at its optimal performance level. She was determined to be young forever.

As part of her treatment, she began implementing detox foot baths. She ordered the foot bath, the cartridges and the salts and began performing the treatments at home. She would do them two – three times a week to assist with draining the toxins out of her body. Each time she found the water ranging from an orange - brownish color. It was absolutely fascinating to watch as the water started out clear and then would become very murky. She would read the color graphs and charts and discover that the foot baths were revealing detoxification from her liver, spleen and joints. Upon completion of each session, she would drink her minerals, which were mixed with her water, to ensure she was putting the good stuff back into her body. She continued this treatment for approximately three months.

Then came the mat sessions. During her visits to the Center, she would lay on a mat for approximately thirty minutes, while oxygen was pumped into her body and cells. This would bring energy frequency, vibrancy, oxygen and recovery to her body, muscles and cells. The sessions assisted her in rehabilitating her nervous system and providing a level of recovery that accelerated her treatment plan.

Anna was given homework each session. She went and she was sure to complete everything she was given. She was practicing her grounding techniques by standing barefoot in the grass and reconnecting with the Earth. At first, she found this difficult to do as her body felt like it was floating more often than not, but with time and persistence she was able to anchor herself into the Earth and bring her anxiety down to a manageable level. She journaled daily and tracked her progress. The tracking logs were used to show the milestone achievements she made over time. This aided both Anna and the practitioners in determining next steps, protocol adjustments and overall confirmation of Anna's recovery.

Anna was feeling so much calmer, healthier and her functionality had improved significantly, and she was now ready to take it to the next level. She had been studying energy, energy work and the power of meditation and manifestation for quite some time. She was completely mesmerized by quantum physics and had become extremely interested in learning all that she could. When she saw that Johnathan, another practitioner at the center, and Nathan were conducting energy sessions with tuning forks using vibrational frequencies, she immediately signed up. She had read and heard so much about the benefits of this type of therapy and thought that perhaps the next step in her journey was to go beyond supplementation and tap into her own energetic field and energy source.

She started out with Jonathan's sessions and saw an immediate change in her vibrational state. For some time, she still had been experiencing the feeling of being plugged into a light socket coursing through her body. She realized at that point in her treatment plan that this was not a health-related fixable issue, this was literally a short in her energetic circuitry. Her body had been holding onto so many trapped emotions and her chakras were out of alignment. The vibrational therapy was the perfect solution for helping her to balance her energy, ground herself and get back into alignment. She was struggling so much in this area, so the sessions were right on time. As she progressed, she began working with Nathan as well, and he began to teach her about restoring her energy to various parts of the body that had been shut off. He was patient and kind as she showed up with her notepad full of questions. She wanted to go beyond the physical realm and really understand the quantum field and energetic exchanges. She learned so much in such a brief period of time.

Then she decided it was time to go a step further. She signed up for the group sound sessions. What an experience. The sessions were designed to provide an intimate group space to immerse the mind, body and spirit in a sound bathing environment. The experience was indescribable. Anna and her daughter signed up for the very first group session and were so in love with the experience that they signed up for many more following the initial class. The sound bathing combined sounds bowls, tuning forks, the didgeridoo, chimes, gongs, seashells, essential oils and the deepest meditation she had ever experienced. It was like going to the amusement park, getting in line, buckling up and enjoying the ride. The first two sessions were very relaxed, calm and she only experienced a few interesting happenings while in the conscious and subconscious space.

The third session was something she would never forget. It was during this session that she was confronted with the darkness. It was so overwhelming and so scary her whole body shook. Linda noticed immediately what was happening and quickly went into action performing energy work to assist Anna with this battle she was fighting. At the end of the session, Linda explained what was happening and Anna shared that during this intense moment of fear she kept repeating that "I walk with God, and you are not welcome here, go away" and eventually all of the images and darkness she saw faded away. This was a huge breakthrough for Anna as she had been working for months on meditations and sessions geared towards addressing some unresolved traumas and was suppressing so much until this moment in time. She left that session feeling so much lighter, so much happier, and so much fuller. That gap of that emptiness that had been consuming her was finally starting to get smaller. She experienced relief on a level way beyond her conscious physical being.

Anna and her daughter continued the sessions beyond the one that had shaken Anna to her core. They decided to keep going because it was a mother-daughter bonding experience and they both were feeling the benefits of healing from all that they had been through. Anna knew it was not just her who had gone through a lot throughout the last several years. She was very cognizant of her children's wellbeing and the impact all of the life experiences they had gone through were having on all of them. Anna had grown to value and respect the wellness center team so much that her children had begun working with the team to improve their health and assist on their spiritual journeys as well. It truly had become a journey to awakening and healing for the whole family.

PART TWO

RE-CREATION REFLECTIONS

THE INNER WORK BEGINS

As Anna continued on her journey, she realized there were areas that she needed to explore that had been unaddressed and no amount of supplementation could fix them. It was during her sessions with the wellness center team that she realized it was time to peel back the onion. The current marriage Anna was in and the quick decline in her health were just symptoms of some deeper issues that had gone unaddressed for years. The pain and suffering she endured in this loveless marriage, filled with misogynistic and narcissistic behaviors and tactics, had felt all too familiar to her. All the relationships before, modeled the same type of issues and challenges. She asked herself over and over again, why would she continue to endure such emotional and psychological abuse? Why? Because it was all too familiar. This chapter in her life ignited all of the flames and hidden darkness that had haunted her soul. Throughout her life and intimate relationships, she had come to learn, experience and accept that love is pain. Oddly enough, she was not even consciously aware of most of what would soon be revealed.

As she began to do the hard work of asking the tough questions, exploring her childhood, performing inner child work, educating herself and seeking the assistance of many on her journey, she began to discover truths about herself and her soul. These answers led to more questions and slowly she was stripped of all she knew in today's physical form and decided to dive deep into her inner experiences that shaped and molded so many limiting beliefs. Because of these accepted and unchallenged beliefs, she had come to adopt and accept unacceptable behaviors and treatment over and over again. This resulted in her placing herself in unhealthy toxic relationships and these relationships served as reinforcements and confirmation of her unconsciously accepted beliefs that love is painful. This cycle continued to reinforce the devaluation of her being.

Anna started with the present day and worked her way backwards slowly. Taking on this type of inner work was going to require a certain amount of honesty and fortitude that she knew was not going to take place overnight. When one chooses to really face their inner demons and fears, and address the unaddressed, there is a certain level of emotional, psychological and physical undoing that takes place. Because Anna had a background in psychology, she knew this part of the journey was going to be challenging. Facing many painful thoughts, memories and feelings was not going to be a walk in the park. In order to be ready for what was to come, she began by preparing, as she always had done when taking on a tough project at work. She got her notebooks ready, downloaded some helpful apps, cleaned her house to clear out any clutter and made sure all the blinds and windows were open, so she had plenty of sunlight and fresh air shining in every single day. She made some playlists of her favorite songs and created a few specific lists that elicited certain memories and moments so that she would find ways to work her way through the emotions. Anna even went out and joined a kickboxing club, because she knew she was going to need to find ways to expend some of the frustration, anger and pain that had built up over time. Anna also identified a strategic list of key players that she felt confident would be able to help her on this tumultuous adventure.

She sought the help of energy healers, homeopathic support, licensed therapists, self-help books and support groups and more. With all of her ducks in a row, she felt it was time to delve deep into her spiritual journey. During this time, it was an opportunity for Anna to do some soul searching, get to know herself and master self-love.

A MATCH MADE IN HELL

First up to address, she started with her present marriage. Why would she stay with someone who clearly had no regard for her and was incapable of loving her? She continued to be emotionally and psychologically abused, always thinking if she just tried a little harder maybe Lionel would love her, be proud of her and notice that all she wanted was to be a priority for him. She would spend hours trying to figure out what she could do to win his affection, be his priority and just live the life that she signed up for the day they married. She would read book after book, have endless conversations with her girlfriend on how to make him happy with her, but all of the solutions she came up with only seemed to be temporary until he got bored with her again. Anna would work harder to help make Lionel's business more profitable and he would give her temporary attention, and then she would have to up the ante to get him to pay attention to her again. Then, she would try to do things for his child, because that always seemed to make him happy for a week or so.

When that wore off, she would pull her funds together and try to jump on the bandwagon with his love for travel and go on more trips. She kept going broke in the process but knew this was a passion of his so she would just keep juggling to make ends meet. There seemed to be a continuous cycle. Lionel would bring her to events and family gatherings where she felt like an outcast and would never stick up for her and always looked at her like she was crazy if she expressed the way she felt in certain situations. It was almost as if she was stuck in this loop of getting breadcrumbs, feeling important to him and then he would toss her aside for others that were serving his purpose at the time. It was like a game of chess, where Lionel simply moved the pieces whichever way he felt, with no given notice, and if she was lucky, she got to be his Queen from time to time. These vicious cycles continued and, like clockwork, every six months he would create a massive fight, threaten to end the marriage and then, have her in tears before he would then tell her he loved her, and he wanted the marriage to work. She fell for it every time... wanting to believe the fairy tale love she had created in her mind with the hopes that it might come true someday. Believing he would make good on all of the promises, hopes and dreams that he had promised her.

Meanwhile, Lionel was running the show the whole time, traveling whenever, with whomever, leaving her behind, staying out all hours of the night, frequenting the strip clubs by himself and, literally, just not giving a damn unless she had something of value to offer him at the time such as taking care of his child, helping with his business or finding new ways to make him more profitable. One night, she discovered he was at a strip club, after he said he was out for his guy's night out to play in his league, he simply brushed it off as if it was not a big deal. He knew how much she did not appreciate him engaging in this behavior. After all, it was not like he was going with a group of guys or for a bachelor party. He simply liked to go until one or two am in the morning by himself, and to Anna that was not acceptable for a married man. It was downright disrespectful. After much deliberation, he finally agreed he would stop going, but he never did...he just got better about covering it up and lying. Meanwhile, he had to know where she was every single second of the day. She could not blink without him knowing it. If she tried to get together with her friends, he would treat her like she was doing something wrong and constantly call her while she was out. Looking at it in retrospect, when conducting a relationship audit, she realized that she was nothing more than an opportunity for him, a possession. Their marriage was a business transaction to him, but to her, he was her everything and she was madly in love with the version of him he presented through his endless love balm behaviors. He sure did know how to put on a show, and he had so many fooled.

He would constantly pick at her about her job and tell her that having a "nine to five" was a joke. The only real way to make money and live life successfully was to own your own business. He would joke about her job not being important and how she should be a millionaire with how smart she was in business, if she had done something different with her life. Meanwhile, her six-figure job was funding a huge portion of the household expenses, the expenses related to supporting her children, because he did not feel they were his to support, especially since she would not let him claim them on his taxes. Gradually, over time, she started to see the inequity in expenses, and he became belligerent with her for bringing it up. Another huge expense that just seemed to increase over time was the endless travel that occurred about every other month.

Anna had a small business as well to provide some additional income as the overwhelming expenses were bleeding her dry. He would constantly talk down about her business and redirect her to help with his, which he expected her to assist with and only offered compensation for the year before they were married. After they married, he said he did not have money to pay her, and it became an expected duty to continue to help him increase his business' profits. While she was working three jobs, he would sit around during the day ordering everyone in the house and his business around, while he would go to the gym, play video games and take naps. As she continued to rack up debt, trying to maintain the lifestyle they were living, he would constantly hound her about her debt and make comments about her financial stress. He would constantly point out her spending habits, which by the way, were mainly for the household and the children. Meanwhile, he was stashing cash and living the high life to position himself for when the relationship would end. If only she had realized his sneaky ways and his total lack of regard for her and her children's interest, but she was oblivious.

Anna loved all of the holidays and opportunities for celebration. Oddly enough, Lionel always found a way to take these special days and put a dark cloud over them. There were several of her birthdays that had gone wrong. She literally began just planning her own birthday celebrations each year, because she knew he was not going to do anything special for her. There was one Christmas that stuck out in her mind...he got her a kitchen faucet to replace the broken faucet in the household kitchen sink. He did not even wrap it. He simply threw it under a coat and told her that her gift was under the coat. She tried to play it off as she saw what it was, but she was truly hurt. Everyone knew how much she put into Christmas and how she would carefully pick each gift for each person and had always wanted someone to do the same for her. She never asked for it, but simply always hoped that someone in her household would care enough about her efforts and reciprocate. When she saw that faucet, she was speechless. She stood in front of the tree with the kids crouched around in shock and simply uttered the words "thank you," because she did not know what else to do.

Another peculiar behavioral theme that kept rearing its ugly head was Lionel's reaction around death and loss. During their time together, Anna had lost several significant key family members and it was his lack of compassion that baffled her and left her feeling completely confused. First was the passing of her grandmother. A woman who had always meant so much to her. They were on vacation and the relationship was still very new. She recalls getting the news and just sitting in silence for a moment when she found out. He initially acted verbally supportive, and then, it was back to vacation. Because the relationship was so new, she did not think too much of it.

She pushed through and handled her grief on her own, not really knowing what to expect from him and being that she was a bit lost in the grieving process herself. When they returned back home, she got together with the family and attended the funeral proceedings, but she had missed her window to sit with her grandmother and say goodbye while she was still here on Earth. This was a moment in time that continues to haunt her. As she knew she should have been there for those final moments.

Then came the loss of his aunt. They would take turns sitting with her in the hospital as she was in her final days, and it was Anna's turn to be at the hospital with her. While she was there, she prayed and prayed for her soul to have peace. She asked God to watch over her and not allow her to go through extended suffering as the cancer had taken over her body. She recalls looking up during prayer and in that moment the monitors sounded, and his aunt stopped breathing. Anna was in total shock. She had never seen death in front of her own eyes, and it was such a scary feeling. When she called him to inform him of the news, he thanked her for letting him know and informed her that he was finishing dinner and would be over after. She was shocked...his aunt, whom he was close with literally just passed and he said he would be there after dinner...what??? She was literally at a loss of what to do...watching the process of someone die is incomprehensible and to be there alone and then receive the nonchalant reaction she did, she was completely confused.

The hardest loss of them all was the later passing of Anna's brother. It was horrific. Anna received the news that her brother had been involved in a terrible accident and had received so much trauma to the head and was not expected to survive. At this point in the relationship, Anna had just fallen ill with several mystery conditions. Unable to drive and unable to really function, her aunt came to pick her up and drive her to see her brother, as he lived several states away. At the hospital, Anna found herself surrounded with her closest family, as the Neuro

ICU allowed limited access to the patients. Lionel did not come on the trip. He decided to stay behind. She felt alone and lost. While everyone else had someone there to lean on she stood alone, confused, distraught and completely numb. So much was happening.

Her brother had been this invisible, strong, protector her whole life and to see him lying there helpless, was beyond Anna's capacity to process. Each day, the doctors would give updates and there were moments with a glimpse of hope and then it would disappear and then the cycle would begin again. A week into the visit, it was necessary for Anna to return home because the pandemic had begun, and things were getting very uncertain from state to state. Anna returned home to find the family in utter chaos. Lionel had picked fights with each of her kids and the first night home was a very heavy and heated discussion, where Lionel declared to everyone that he was God, and everyone had to obey him. He became belligerent and began saying very mean and hateful things to Anna and the children.

Anna tried to diffuse the situation the best she could, but she was in no mental state to be able to deal with this type of pressure after spending a long draining week watching her brother take some of his last breaths. To come home to this madness was completely disrespectful and uncalled for, and she barely had the strength to get through it.

Over the next few days, she received the reports from the family about her brother's status and when it was time to remove the lifesaving mechanisms she was patched in through facetime, where she would ultimately watch her brother pass from this Earth to Heaven.

It was during this time that she was in her room, glued to the iPad watching his every breath and Lionel came in and asked if she would like to go to his sisters to discuss the stock market. She looked at him in utter disbelief. Was he serious?!? He knew what was going on and literally said, "Okay, I'll see you in a bit." Anna was in such a state of disbelief, completely emotionally distraught and had been battling this mystery illness that she simply did not have the strength to fight or argue with him. It was all she could do to collect herself, go through the motions and be there for her family.

This was truly a time in history that will be etched in her mind forever. It was truly one of the most tragic experiences by far that she had ever gone through, and she found herself completely alone. The only thing she could do was pray, cry and beg God to bring her brother to Heaven where he belonged. His life had been so much harder than it ever should have been, and he did not deserve to go out of this life the way it happened. It was completely wrong and she and everyone around her knew it, and to watch it happen and then to see the complete and utter lack of compassion from her spouse was eye opening for sure.

Then there was the constant focus on her weight. She would work out two – three hours a day...lots of cardio, hired personal trainers and just could not keep the weight off when she became ill. He made comments such as, "I guess I can tolerate you being heavier if you are sick." He would constantly try to push her at the gym and force his workout plans on her and watch what she ate. She would try to work out with her girlfriend, and he would constantly come over and increase the speed on the treadmill and tell her they were not working out hard enough. It was as if he just could not let her be, as if he was disgusted by her.

Lionel knew when he met her that she was a curvy girl, but for some reason he did not seem satisfied with that unless she was a size four/six. Maintaining this size was becoming unattainable, as she struggled with fluctuating hormone levels after having surgery to ensure she could not have children since that was such a huge topic of discussion in the early part of the relationship. This had, in essence, sent her body into an early menopause state, which made weight loss a true chore. She lived off of laxatives for a good year, trying to keep the weight off that she had lost from the trainer leading up to and following their wedding. She would just keep working out harder and harder, despite Lionel's constant desire to keep going out to restaurants and eating at all hours of the day and night. It was actually quite humorous that he constantly chastised her for the lifestyle she was living, the foods she ate and her children's weight, yet they had never eaten out so much until they met him and she had never found herself in so many social situations that always surrounded her with foods that were not exactly designed to keep one's figure slim. Because he was not gaining weight and was able to maintain his weight, it was okay for him to keep carrying on, and she was supposed to be there, but I guess not participate. So why in the hell would she stay in such a toxic relationship?

After she went through several rounds of protocols and began to feel stronger, she realized what she had to do. She had to save herself and her children and walk away from the abusive marriage she was in. Anna knew now if she did not leave it would be the death of her, literally, and she still had so much to do on this Earth. Through several conversations with God, she realized He wanted more for her and that she did not belong in this relationship. She was holding herself to a standard that she thought God expected from her and realized that God never wanted her to be in a relationship, let alone a marriage that was slowly killing her soul and to stay with a man who was trying to claim her life.

After a huge fight that Lionel started, she decided to take him up on his harsh words that they should just be done, and she informed him that she would leave with her children and get out of his way. She knew that was what he and his child had wanted anyway so she made it easy for them. She asked for nothing in return other than to leave with herself, her children and her income intact. Again, she took on a substantial amount of debt that they had racked up together. Of course, he did not feel that he had any responsibility to her or her children because he was clever with his financial secrets, and of course, since many of the debts were in her name or hidden using other's names, he felt he was cleared of any obligation. She did not ask for anything from him, nothing from his business, nothing from his home, she simply scraped what she had left together and went and rented a home for her and her children to stay in while they began to rebuild their lives.

Lionel's life and the life of his child were not disrupted as they got to carry on with business as usual. As for Anna and her children, they had to start over AGAIN and figure it all out. She wanted nothing and took nothing that belonged to him. Anna could not believe it was over and that it had ended this way. All she truly wanted was his heart, his love and the promise of forever together. There was nothing he could give her, or she could take that would fill the void and the enormous amount of pain she felt as she watched her dreams fall apart. She had not entered into this relationship or marriage for anything other than love.

HER FIRST ATTEMPT AT FOREVER

At the young age of eighteen, Anna had gone away to college in the Washington, DC area. She was quite far from home and had no friends or family in the area and felt alone. Since Anna was from a small town, she could not quite get comfortable with the big city life concept. About halfway into her first semester, she met a man named Frank who was much older than her, and they immediately began seeing one another. Several months in they began dating and fell in love. Anna had no concept of the real world or what life had in store for her. She just knew that she was far from home and had found someone whom she cared for deeply and it was not long after her freshman year that things became quite serious. When she returned home that summer her parents were not exactly thrilled to hear that their daughter had fallen in love with a man quite a bit older than her. Her mother gave her an ultimatum to stop dating him and she would continue to pay for college, or she could keep dating him and figure it out herself. Anna was very stubborn and certainly did not like being told what to do so she took the latter option and left. With no plan in mind, she headed back to the big city to figure out how she was going to pay for college and where she was going to live.

Anna moved in with Frank and was able to register for school by taking out student loans. She could not afford to cover tuition and live on campus so living with Frank seemed the next best option. She continued pursuing her education and from there began working full-time while going to school full-time. In her second year of college, Anna and Frank were still going strong and Frank decided to propose to Anna. They were wed that summer and soon after they began discussing having a family. They welcomed their first child the summer going into her last year of college.

Throughout the development of their early years of marriage, Anna began to notice a change in Frank. He was not as kind and loving as he had been when they were dating. His demeanor would change when things did not go the way he wanted them to. He had a quick temper and would go from laughing and joking to becoming very boisterous and domineering. Frank drank a lot. He would justify it by saying it was only beer but could crush a twelve-pack like it was nothing. It first started out as a six-pack and then when the weekend came, all bets were off. He would smoke cigarettes and marijuana daily and it was starting to affect their marriage. The drinking and smoking were too much for Anna to handle. She was no longer a young and inexperienced college kid. She was a full-time student, full-time employee, wife and mother and this was not the type of household she had envisioned.

Frank would often make Anna sit down while he lectured her for hours about how she should be doing things and what life should be looking like. She was very confused by his change in behavior and was not sure what to do. After a more serious argument, which resulted in getting a little more physical than she had ever experienced with him, they both realized that this relationship was not healthy, and Anna knew she could not go on like this. She struggled with what to do, because she had been brought up Catholic and knew how serious marriage was and she had made a promise to God, herself and her husband and she did not take promises lightly. They eventually sought the assistance of a religious counselor who specialized in working with couples and anger management. Frank was a smooth talker and was able to fool the counselor into thinking that it was Anna who was the one misinterpreting his intentions. Despite the holes in the wall, from where he would put his fist through when he was angry, and the belittling that would happen when he would yell at her, she realized the problem would not be solved here.

As the years went on, Anna realized this was definitely not what she had in mind for her happily ever after. A few years into the marriage they were blessed with their second child. A pleasant surprise and Anna was overjoyed. She loved being a mom and she knew that this little bundle of joy was a gift from God. Her husband was surprised by the news, but after his initial reaction and shock, he warmed up to the idea of having another little one running around the house. This would be his third child, as he had a child from a previous marriage. Once the baby arrived, more turmoil ensued. Frank continued to become more irritable, and Anna just kept going. Finances were tight, childcare costs were outrageous and, at this point, Anna was working on her Master's degree while working full-time and still going to school full-time.

Fast forward a few more years later, and God decided to bless Anna and Frank with their third child. Frank was not as accepting of this and had decided to make plans to ensure that would be their last. He was a bit distant during this pregnancy and Anna began to feel more and more alone, wondering what she had signed up for. How was this a partnership...how was this love? As the years went on, she found herself doing the majority of the child raising. He would go to work, come home, sometimes cook and sometimes sit and watch football or sports. He would sit out in the car and smoke or go visit the neighbors. Meanwhile, Anna would be left to do dinner, baths, run the kids to and from their activities and handle all of the administrative household operations.

As the years went on, she began to feel lonelier and lonelier. She recalled lugging all of the little ones into church one Sunday and staying in the back "cry room" where all of the parents with young children sat and sat there wondering what people thought when they saw her there with all the kids by herself. She used to dream up excuses like...maybe they think their father is in the military and away. There was one very sweet couple who would always offer to help her back to the car, because she looked a little disheveled with a baby in a car seat, a two- year-old on her hip and a four-year-old clinging to her leg. She was embarrassed and ashamed that she did have a spouse who just was not there for her and the children like many of the other church families.

Sadly, Anna's life did not get much easier. She was charged with figuring out how to make ends meet. Her husband would work overtime and take odd jobs, but, because she had all of the college education and work experience, she was left to be the bread winner and make magic happen. She longed for the support of an equal partner, but again, knew that she had made a commitment and she was doing all that she could to give her children the life she had dreamed of for them. That life did not include divorce, as she knew that she did not want her children to have to experience life the way she had growing up.

Anna gave it all she could. She pushed through the years. Put the kids in private school like her husband had wanted. She was part of all of the school boards and activities. She had them in sports and ran and ran and ran. She was exhausted and felt emotionally depleted. She recalled having to have foot surgery and asking her mom to come down to help her post- surgery because her husband said he could not take off of work and she was not sure how she was supposed to do it with the kids, work and the 6-week healing process. Thankfully, her mother obliged, but she realized that her husband really was not that concerned about helping her or even being there for her during this time.

They would travel up to see Anna's family for holidays and a short getaway, and every time they did Frank would always complain. He would stay in the bedroom, hide away from the family or just simply act disinterested. There was one particular visit where he had a little too much to drink and began swearing at Anna's mother. This was the moment that she realized she could not do this anymore. He had taken it too far. She could not allow him to disrespect her family in this manner. It was bad enough he would always disrespect her, but what he was doing now was out of control. They again sought help for his behavior and for a while, things seemed to be a bit better.

The moment of truth came when Anna was involved in a car accident. She was hit from behind by a large truck while at a complete stop. The accident changed Anna's life and perspective forever. She called Frank, desperately, while at the scene because she knew something was very wrong. He did not answer, which was unusual because he was always on the phone with her, and he was always calling to see where she was and what she was doing. Anna ended up calling her friend and asked her to come to the scene. The ambulances and fire trucks had arrived, but Anna did not want to go with the medics, because she had her children with her as she was heading to pick up her eldest from band practice. Although Anna was a bit out of sorts, the officer agreed to let her drive home, since she was only a few minutes from the house, if her friend followed close behind.

When she got home, Frank was there and nonchalantly said, "Okay, let's go to urgent care and have you looked at to make sure you are good to go." Upon initial evaluation, the doctors determined she had a concussion in addition to whiplash and some injuries to her lower back. Anna was quite scared, because she realized that this was going to require lots of medical appointments, physical therapy and potentially some long-term nerve issues. As they left the doctor's office, scared, Anna asked Frank why he was so quiet. He snapped and said he was irritated because now he had missed dinner, it was late, and everything was closed so he could not pick something up. Anna was baffled. She literally had just found out she had a concussion and several injuries, and his only concern was that he had not had dinner and it was late. Seriously?!?

Per the doctor's orders, Anna was not to be left alone and required monitoring for the next twenty-four to forty-eight hours for the concussion. Frank quickly let her know that he could not miss work the next day so she would need to figure it out. So, Anna decided to go to work, and hopped in her vanpool so that at least at work there were medical staff present and she would be monitored. The craziest solution ever, but it was the best one she could think of in the current situation. For the next several months, Anna relied upon her friend to help her with getting the kids back and forth to school, helping with her doctor's appointments, completion of medical forms, etc., since she was really struggling to function as a result of the concussion.

A few months after the accident she decided she could not do it anymore. It was time for a divorce. She could not fathom spending the rest of her life with someone who had such little regard for his wife, the mother of his children and the woman who had done everything she could to be a great wife and make his life more comfortable. For goodness sakes, she would have to cut the grass for their almost two-acre yard every other weekend so that he could sit comfortably in the house and watch football.

The neighbors were disgusted by this site. As she approached him and let him know that she could not do this anymore he became very upset. He was not willing to accept what she was saying at all. Over the next few weeks, he realized she was serious, and he contacted her doctor. He told her doctor that he believed the concussion had affected her judgement and that something was wrong because she wanted a divorce. Her doctor reached out to her and had a discussion with her about what was going on. Anna was very surprised by the doctor's call and Anna let her know that she had lived in a home with a man who drank too much, smoked, screamed and spit in her face (what he called having a discussion), had several holes in the wall from where he put his fist through and would constantly belittle her and the children. Needless to say, after that conversation, the doctor apologized and assured her that she was simply reaching out to check on her to make sure she was okay.

Throughout the divorce process, it got nasty. Exactly what Anna did not want to happen, happened. The kids were subjected to so much turmoil. Frank was not too concerned about using discretion about their separation. When Frank moved out, he began to talk negatively about Anna to the kids and even began to pick on the child that looked most like her mother. He would create arguments with Anna in front of the children and they would just cry. It was very unhealthy. The divorce process was longer than necessary, because he would request changes over and over again to drag out the process. He did not get a lawyer, so Anna's bill just kept piling higher and higher with each change he requested to the agreements. She asked for nothing in the divorce outside of keeping her own finances, her children to reside with her and she took all of the joint debts. She did feel bad about not delivering forever with the man she married, and she realized freedom was not free, so her way of rationalizing the ending of the marriage was to take all the debt to minimize some of the burden felt by her spouse. After the divorce, the relationship between Frank and Anna did not become any better.

After the marriage ended, Anna put herself back out on the dating circuit. She had not given up on love and she knew there was a man somewhere out there for her. She joined a single's group that organized events and adventures for singles in the DC area to come together and meet. She attended an event and that is where she met Lionel. Soon after, they began their relationship. During this time, Frank became more difficult to deal with and eventually he began to pick fights with her and try to pin the kids against her. He would try to pin them against each other by saying and doing things that made them jealous of one another. At one point, their son decided to go stay with him for a while, as there were some disagreements between him and his later stepfather. Anna had chalked this up to a teenage boy becoming a man and did not really fully understand what mind games Lionel was playing, as this was before she began to understand who he truly was under the mask.

With Anna and the kids in a new home and a new relationship, Frank's temper did not lessen. Anna recalled going to pick the kids up one night from him and he became totally engulfed in a fit of rage when she addressed his inappropriate discussions with the children. He pinned her to her car and became so verbally abusive that the neighbors came out to see what was going on. She barely made it into the car without him, almost smashing his hand through her back window, where their youngest child was sitting, before he chased her car down the street. It was insanity.

What complicated matters further was the endless back and forth in court over the settlement of the family home that they still co-owned. There was a lack of cooperation on Frank's part to sell the home once the property settlement agreement, which was part of the divorce agreement, had reached its maturity terms and conditions. He did everything possible to complicate the sale of the home. Anna eventually had to get the courts involved and have a trustee appointed to manage the sale of the home. It got totally out of hand, but she knew this was just another way of Frank's determination to complicate her life. Anna muddled through the process and did her best to maintain a positive outlook and just go through the motions.

This was a relationship that was built on a fantasy. Because Anna was so young when she began her life with Frank, she realized she did not have the life experience to fully understand what she had gotten herself into. It did not help that there was so much turmoil between Anna and her family at the beginning of the relationship and she felt like she had to prove a point. After moving in with Frank, the natural progression of life seemed to take the lead, and marriage seemed like the next logical step. It was not until it was too late that she realized she had bitten off more than she could chew. She walked away from the relationship feeling guilty and ashamed for not being able to uphold the promise she had made before God. She was not a quitter, and it was really hard for her to admit defeat in this instance. All she knew was this was not what she wanted for her or her children. She did not want her daughters growing up thinking it was the woman's job to mow the lawn while her husband sat and watched TV. It was not the woman's job to hold down the family while the man did whatever he wanted and showed up just in time for the family pictures. She figured if she was going to be a married single mom, she might as well be a single mom without the extra adult child sucking her dry.

HER PREVIOUS RELATIONSHIPS

Prior to her marriages, Anna had engaged in relationships that, by her definition, were considered long-term relationships. She had dated the same guy in high school for three years and the guy after him was a one and a half-year relationship. Both of these relationships were filled with lies, deception and infidelity. Both, where she was doing 80 percent of the work and receiving breadcrumbs of love and attention that she had come to think was enough. Her wants and desires were minimized, and she became just another actress in the play. One resounding feeling was true in these relationships as well...she always felt alone in the relationship. One of her favorite Broadway musicals was Les Misérables and one of her favorite songs from the play was "On My Own". She used to sing it over and over and felt it to her core. This song could not have played out truer in her romantic relationships.

The guys she had attracted and dated sexualized her and had the charm that kept her believing they cared. She began to believe her value was measured by their expectations and standards. Anna transformed herself into whatever the situation called for in an attempt to please her partners. Despite her best efforts, it was never enough. They always started out the same...she would meet the men when she was at her best and had everything going for her. She had shared her hopes and dreams, they had played the game and acted supportive and interested. She had opened her heart, confided in them and showed her true self. She would be wooed, swept off her feet and then, once she got in too deep, things would change rapidly.

In the case of her marriages, it literally changed the day the marriage papers were signed. She found herself no longer in a space of love and growth, but quickly realized she had become property. In her first marriage she learned this the very first night.

She had family in town to participate in the wedding and, since they did not travel often, she was excited to see them and wanted to go out that evening to celebrate and show them around the city. Frank was not interested in that option at all, he became very belligerent and began yelling at her, and pushed her on the bed and told her that is not what she was going to be doing on her wedding night. He made it very clear that their wedding night was about them and that her family could wait. She was not totally against spending the night consummating their marriage, but she was a bit perplexed, as they had been living together for quite some time and the family was only in town for two days and she really had hoped that they could all spend some time together celebrating. They had a whole lifetime together, but only a few short days with the family. Needless to say, she did not get to spend time with her family and felt embarrassed and ashamed when she had to call them and let them know there had been a change in plans and they would not be getting together that evening.

Then there was the second marriage, it was a bit more subtle, but it slowly started with demanding the changes of her looks, no more make-up, dressing a certain way and doing "as she was told," versus being an independent thinker. All of a sudden, she no longer had a name, and she was just referred to as "my wife". At first it seemed cute, but then others started to notice that she was never addressed as Anna, and the references and demeanor seemed to reveal a very property-based referral when he spoke about or to her. He would say things like, "No wife of mine would do that," or "I do not want a wife that behaves like that." It was such an interesting and surprising way to address her. Even her friends had stopped him to say..." Are you talking about Anna?" and he would respond with "my wife." It was almost like she had become a "thing" versus a "person." She longed to hear him just say her name once in a while, but he barely ever spoke her name after they became married. At first, she thought it was because he had experienced a pretty serious seizure not long before their wedding. She had mentioned to the doctor during the follow-ups that he had seemed to become a bit colder and shorter fused the weeks following the episode. Both Lionel and the doctor dismissed her observations and that was that. He then began to start watching videos on "how a wife should behave," and "what she should do," and he would constantly pick at Anna and tell her what he expected of her. The level of male chauvinistic behavior just kept escalating. He always expressed what he wanted and had no interest in her thoughts or feelings.

In each of the relationships, Anna's strong independent personality would slowly diminish over time. She would go from being this strong, confident, badass woman, who could take on anything, to this submissive, weak, pathetic being, who could barely function by the time the relationships were ending. It was as if a part of her soul was killed with each new relationship and intimate experience. The sad part was, no matter how hard she tried, Anna could not find it in her heart to have malintent for the men who had so deeply wronged her. She would simply walk away each time figuring it was her fault and something was wrong with her. She shouldered the burden of the failed relationship, each time and with each continued defeat, she felt less and less confident in her ability to find a healthy love that would resemble the fairy tale she had dreamed of since she was a little girl.

The culmination of these relationships continued to reinforce Anna's limiting beliefs that love is pain and left her full of scars and wounds that just kept piling up as the years went on. Anna began to believe she was not worthy of love and that she must have done something wrong to keep having the same results.

She just figured she needed to try harder and do better and be what the men in her life were looking for because apparently, who and what she was did not seem to be working out for her. Anna did not have a demonstration of a healthy relationship to compare her experiences to so this just seemed more of the same. She seemed to carry this energetic vibration into her future intimate relationships by attracting love interests with similar traits.

It was the limiting beliefs and misalignment with her or the source, her higher power, God, and her soul that was really the challenge. There was nothing wrong with Anna, other than the fact that she was trying to conform to each of the men's unrealistic expectations and to be what they wanted her to be, versus being who she truly was. She had spent her life being a people pleaser and searching for romantic love to have the deep human connection she always yearned for as a child.

REVISITING HER CHILDHOOD

Surely, Anna did not wake up one day and just decide that she would enjoy engaging in unhealthy relationships that were toxic to her soul. In order to begin connecting the dots, she knew she needed to go back to the beginning. Anna had a background in psychology and knew that every struggle and challenge in a person's life can be traced back to childhood. So, Anna revisited her childhood to find the answers. To assist with making this process more manageable, she solicited the support of professionals to ensure she was able to be prepared for and work through all of her discoveries. She had a lot to unpack, things that she had bottled up, pushed down and hidden away for far too long and this amount of work was certain to stir up some unexpected emotions and feelings. Knowing this, she wanted to ensure she had all of the support available to her to make the process a little more manageable.

Anna grew up in a small town. She had an older and younger sibling. The town was a quiet little quaint place where everyone knew everyone. Her parents were both middle-class Americans who had earned their way to the top. They had both come from two-parent households. She was brought up Catholic and her mother regularly took her and her siblings to church every Sunday. Her father would joke and say he was good, he did not need to go, because he attended St. Mattress. The family would gather with aunts, uncles, cousins and friends very regularly having barbeques, pool parties and celebrations. There were not many weekends that were not filled with family gatherings. There was no shortage of what felt like "family love" in the early years of her upbringing.

This all came to a crashing halt when Anna turned ten. Her parents decided to divorce, and Anna and her siblings were devastated. It all happened so suddenly. They did not understand what had gone wrong. One day they were one big happy family and, out of nowhere, this all changed. Her father made it very clear that he was not in favor of the divorce and quickly began accusing Anna's mother of all kinds of things. The children became caught in the middle and were not sure who was telling the truth and what was really going on. They had not even seen their parents ever fight and were not aware of all of the adult conversations and unhealthy, toxic behaviors occurring behind closed doors. They were good at hiding what was really going on.

The children were split between the two parents. Anna was devastated when her oldest brother left the home to go with her father and she and her younger brother remained with their mom. The transition was not an easy one. Anna missed both her brother and her father. She was very close to her older brother and looked up to him. He always looked out for her and kept her safe, like any great big brother would do. She always wanted to hang out with him and his friends, and like any older sibling would feel, who wants their little sister tagging along everywhere, that totally deflates the coolness factor when hanging out with your friends. The night he left with their father, he came and sat with her for quite some time. She sat and cried, begging him not to go. He told her she would be okay and promised her that everything would work out. She knew in her heart that was not true. She knew he would not be there when she woke up, would not be at the bus stop to look out for her, would not be there to sit at the breakfast and dinner table each day.

Who was she supposed to talk to? Her little brother would spend time together with her, but he was younger than her and the relationship she had with him was different than with her older brother. She was the protector for her little brother, and in most instances, the second mom. She would take care of him when her mom was not around and was always looking out for him. As she sat on the bed that night and cried herself to sleep, she felt alone and lost. Why was this happening? How could God let this happen to her family? How could her brother just leave? Why was her dad taking him from her? The years to follow did not get any easier. As a matter of fact, they just got more complicated and served as scenario after scenario supporting her limiting beliefs that love is pain.

Anna was treated like a rag doll being pulled in every direction by her parents. She was constantly fighting for her father's attention, while her mother was short, fused with having to shoulder the burden of being the mother and the father of the household. She was angry at both of them for not being able to make it work and putting her in this impossible position, where she constantly felt like she had to pick sides. The strained relationship between her parents' post-divorce created such angst in her life. She and her brothers felt torn and there was such a lack of harmony. Her older brother grew more distant to her mother and had even become very physical with her, because of his anger and the continuous negative things he would hear about their mother. Anna and her younger brother were constantly defending their mother to him, which only added fuel to the fire. He would become angry with them and not want anything to do with them. The relationship became strained, yet Anna knew if she ever needed him, he would be there for her.

Constant criticism and feelings of "not being good enough" ruminated in Anna's mind constantly. Why did her father leave them? Why was she not worthy of his attention? Why did her brother go with him and not want to stay with them? Why did her mom want to break up the family? Was it the right decision? Anna's child version could only see the family struggles from a limited perspective, as she was just a young girl. So many questions and no answers. She did not talk about it, because there was already so much for everyone to deal with that it was just easier to bury her feelings and put a big smile on her face and pretend everything was okay. Her grandfather would always tell her "Smile, you have such a pretty smile." So, she learned that is what she needed to do, just put on a happy face. Anna became really good at pretending everything was okay, and she even had convinced herself it was, despite feeling dead inside. This just became her coping mechanism...her way of life. She even created make believe friends to talk to, because at least they would listen to her. She did not really believe they were real, but it was comforting for her to think there was someone there listening to her.

As part of the divorce agreement, it was determined that the children would go to therapy to ensure they adjusted to the new family norm. Anna would attend the sessions and really was not thrilled about it. She would discuss random things like school, her career aspirations, and anything and everything, but how she truly felt. She just figured it did not matter and she really did not have a frame of reference of how families, relationships and divorces were supposed to go since she was just a kid. Every time she was with her father, he would bash her mother and when she was with her mother, she was short fused and did not want to talk about things. She was just so frustrated with Anna always being angry all the time and a challenge to deal with. Anna recalled the therapist expressing that Anna only expressed a limited scale of emotions – anger, sadness and happiness. She was not too concerned, because that meant nothing to her, she had learned to numb her feelings, so it sounded like those were the three most appropriate if she had to choose...oh and, by the way...how many emotions are there anyways? Because Anna was so good at keeping a smile on her face, and presented herself as a well-adjusted child, no one really dug too much into what was really going on with her. She was at the top of her class, involved in social clubs, athletics and school government. Her teachers, family and friends did not have many negative things to say so she appeared to be a typical kid for her age, minus the fact that there was a broken home that had devastated her heart.

During this time of transition in Anna's life, there was a lot of chaos and shuffling of the kids from place to place. Anna was very active in sports and school activities, so she was out of the home a lot. People naturally gravitated towards her, and she would light up the room wherever she went. Various family members helped her single mother with watching the kids, providing love and support and they did everything they could to support the family through all of the madness. Sadly, during this time period, because there was so much going on, and Anna was doing her best to lie low and not cause any more stress than her mother was already experiencing, things got very dicey in Anna's life. She found herself being compromised and sexually molested at an early age. Because she was so confused by what had happened to her, she kept it to herself. She did not know what to do or where to go. If she said anything, would anyone believe her? Was this supposed to be happening? Was she at fault for what had happened? What would people think of her? As all of these questions swarmed in her mind, she decided that again, it was just best to keep her head down and keep going and not cause any problems. This happened to her on more than one occasion, and it was not isolated to one person, there were others. Anna began to experience physical symptoms as a result of the abuse. She began having many bladder infections and lots of intestinal issues. During this time, she had been diagnosed with Lyme disease, and the doctors could not figure out what was really going on. Although, her diagnosis of Lyme took months and months because she had so many identifiable symptoms like chronic fatigue, constant dizzy spells, intestinal issues and just not functioning properly. It was during this time period in her life that Anna received her first lessons in betrayal, mixed with confusion about what love is, what it looks like, and the broken trust appeared in her life. These acts would later be the moments that created so many limiting beliefs surrounding intimate relationships.

As the years went on, Anna would dream of what life would be like when she grew up and she was in charge of her life. She would get her dog that her mom never wanted to have, because she was not a fan of animals. She was going to grow up one day and have three children and a family of her own and she was going to get it right. She was going to have the white house, picket fence...the all-American family. While all of her friends began to explore and discuss what they wanted to be when they grew up, she redirected the conversation to wanting the family that she never had. She was never concerned or even put much thought into what her career would be when she grew up. She came from a family of business owners and success came naturally to her. Not once did she consider having any challenges in the professional area of her life, so she never put any emphasis on it. As she got closer to the end of high school, she explored career options and decided she wanted to pursue her dream of becoming a Clinical Psychologist owning her own Practice. She figured that way, she could help others, on a deeper level, who experienced pain and suffering in their lives.

Then came the self-image issues. During puberty she developed faster than the other girls and did not have the shape of Barbie, so she was looked at differently, as all the girls her age were still skinny twigs. She had a very curvaceous body and did not quite fit the mold of her peers. Her grandfather would constantly pick at her and grab her sides and stomach and tell her she was getting fat. Her parents would frequently make comments about her getting too heavy as well. Meanwhile, their version of too heavy was a little over one-hundred pounds. One boy in particular that she had a crush on would tease and taunt her for being so developed since she was the first of her peers to develop a chest and a butt. One day, after being taunted on the bus, she went home and taught herself how to shave her legs, which turned out to be a bloody mess. She also led her peers in starting her menstrual cycle and was traumatized by it, because she had no clue what was going on when it happened. The teacher sent her to the school nurse and the school nurse explained what was happening. What a fun day that was and what a way to welcome womanhood.

The culmination of all of these events was the beginning of her long unhealthy relationship with her body and with food. She would walk by the mirror and look at her figure in disgust. The funny thing was, her peers wished they had the shape she did, but Anna felt ashamed of what she saw. This was the figure that drew the attention of grown men, made her feel like an outcast and left her feeling embarrassed. She began exercising constantly, walking for hours after school, playing sports to get in more physical exercise and she would wake up around two am at night and complete her ab routine and her "Abs and Buns of Steel" videos. When it came to her diet...she first went the anorexic route. That was going well, she had lost weight and seemed to hear less about her size for a while. Suddenly her menstrual cycles stopped and to the doctors she went. The doctors told her she would be put away in a hospital if she did not start eating, because she had gotten to a dangerous unhealthy weight. The thought of being put away was enough to scare her and she began eating immediately.

It was not an easy process for her, because she had developed such a fear of food and its implications on the scale. So, her chapter with anorexia was closed, but it did not stop there though, she needed to maintain an "acceptable" weight by the standards of her family and peers, so she began the unhealthy behavior of bulimia. She figured if she could not be anorexic to maintain her weight and the long workouts and middle of the night workouts were not yielding results, she would then binge and purge. Anna became skilled at sneaking away to the bathroom after meals and had begun with the toothbrush trick to expel the food she would eat with the family at the dinner table. Eventually, she had gotten so good at it that she no longer needed the toothbrush, and her gag reflex was an automatic response. This all seemed like a good solution at the time, no one was teasing her about her weight, and she had a strategy that was accomplishing and helping her stick to her weight and image goals.

Anna felt so much pressure in her growing years. She became an overachiever...getting the best grades...being the best at the sports she played in...President of her class...member of student government...the list goes on. If she got an A, it was looked upon as why was not an A+? Her family was very well known in the town, and she knew it was her job to make sure she kept her nose to the ground, stay out of trouble and did not bring negative attention to the family. She could not go anywhere without people reporting back to her parents. This was a perfect storm for the feeling of having to be perfect. The thought of disappointing her family was a tremendous burden to bear.

Anna's teen years did not get any easier. She turned to drinking, smoking cigarettes and desperately seeking out relationships to numb the void and pain she felt at home. She found that when she drank or smoked cigarettes it gave her a rush that made her feel alive inside. She had felt so dead inside and she was desperately searching for anything to make her feel. As the years continued to progress, more sadness and pain continued to enter Anna's life.

Her freshman year of high school, a dear friend had passed away unexpectedly, and it left Anna questioning how this could happen to someone so young and with such a good heart. He was a star of the football team, loved by all and one of the strongest people she knew. He had the biggest heart and was such an amazing guy. The entire high school felt the pain of his loss. The funeral was such an overwhelming experience. The building was packed, people were lined up outside and several had to be taken by ambulance after having complete emotional breakdowns at the ceremony.

That loss was followed by one of her best friends being diagnosed with cancer. This was more than she could comprehend, why...why was this all happening? She watched her friend battle cancer with strength and might that she was sure she would pull through and be fine. She did so and had gone into remission and then it came back, and she ultimately lost her battle. It was devastating, they had known each other since kindergarten.

Then there was her uncle, her Godfather, whom she adored. One morning, the phone rang, and it was her aunt calling to inform the family that her uncle had had a stroke. He was unresponsive and had been rushed to the hospital. The verdict was not looking good and there were so many arguments over whether or not to take him off the ventilator or wait longer to see if he became conscious. Anna spent several days and nights staying by her uncle's side at the hospital. He was so young, only in his early 30s and had three small children. Again, why was this happening? Why? Her aunt decided that she was not going to pull the plug on him, and that God would get to the make the decision. He regained consciousness and was completely immobilized and could not speak. He spent months in a rehabilitation center only to come out with half of his body immobile and never to speak again.

Not long after her Uncle's stroke, her grandfather was rushed to the hospital due to experiencing a massive heart attack. Again, the verdict did not look good. He needed a quadruple bypass, and the doctors were not certain if his health was good enough for him to pull through. Surprisingly, he made it through the surgery and recovered. The months that followed were long and daunting. This shook the family up as well, as he was a very domineering man and was the patriarch of the family. Now, with him down and one of his sons unable to function from his recent stroke, the family was starting to fall apart. The family business was in jeopardy and Anna began to fear for the health and safety of all around her. So much was happening so quickly and without warning. She felt so scared. Who was next?

Then, there was the loss' her older brother experienced, a close friend, who committed suicide by hanging himself, another one who committed suicide soon after. Another tragic incident was when one of his former girlfriends, who had become part of the family, had gotten into a terrible accident following a fight they had. As a result of the accident, she was paralyzed from the waist down and never walked again. Soon after the car accident, Anna's younger brother's friend committed suicide. So much sadness and death in such a brief period of time.

During this time, Anna began to bury her emotions further and further inside. She had learned to cope using a strategy that was coming from a place of numbness. It was easier to not feel than it was to experience the pain of loss of the ones she loved. She did not know how to talk about the loss of her friends or the emptiness it left in her heart. Love in all forms had become so painful. First, it was the loss of her family unit, then came the loss of a dear friend, and then the loss of her best friend and so on. Despite all of the pain, she continued to push forward, shining her light and spreading love wherever she went.

Anna had tried her hand at romantic love and poured her heart and soul into that to help ease the pain of life's cruelty. She thought she had found "the one." Because when you are a teenager, you believe that love will last forever, and some high school sweethearts do, but the odds of that happening were not in her favor. She spent three years investing all she had into the relationship only to find out he had been sleeping around with several others. He made a complete mockery and fool out of her. Her heart was shattered and to make matters worse, she found out about the cheating in the most unexpected way. Anna felt so low, as if it were her fault, and now, who was going to want her? She felt disgusted and alone. Everyone knew them as a couple and had found out about the cheating, and it became a public embarrassment for Anna. She tried to exercise forgiveness and tried to work through the devastating betrayal, and she did until she could not anymore. She eventually gained enough strength to realize she deserved better, and she was worth more than what he was willing to offer. Again, she associated the love she had so willingly given with the result ending the same as all the others...in pain.

As Anna stood in the Church Hall on her Confirmation Day, she decided to speak with the priest during the reception. She could not help but ask how to navigate such negativity in the world and in life. She had gone through so many painful events. They just started to feel like the norm. She was troubled though by the darkness in her world. She felt the heaviness of the negative energy in her being and she was looking for spiritual guidance. He shared some biblical references with her and encouraged her not to let the darkness affect her light. As logical as this all sounded to her, it seemed so difficult to apply. She had seen so much, experienced so much and the majority of it had been very unhealthy, toxic, negative and heart breaking. She did vow not to let her light, go out and to keep pushing forward, but she still had some hesitation in her mind.

On to the dysfunctional toxic family traits and behaviors. Everyone in her family owned their own businesses and could not fathom working for anyone else. The requirement for power and prestige superseded all! Family gatherings were very much a "whose more important than who" moment. Conversations stemmed around who had the nicest car, whose kids had which job and where were everyone's kids going to school. So, when Anna went away to college, where she was far from home, alone, confused and not sure what was in store for her. The cards seemed stacked against her, but she was determined to prove her self-worth by being the biggest overachiever ever. When she finished her degree, she pushed further and kept going and obtained two more graduate degrees, just to validate her value. After finishing her first graduate degree, she decided to join the workforce, many in her family were surprised. They did not expect her to do that. Even though she landed a fantastic job it was still a bit of unspoken disappointment.

To add to the shock of it all...to the family...Anna had married a man who was older than her and outside of her race. This was received differently by each of the family members. Some of the older generational family members were not as thrilled about her choice. Having mixed children added another dimension to the whole story. Anna decided it would be best to remain down in the big city where she was versus moving back home to where she came from. She did not feel like there was anything there for her and given her life choices, she did not feel that her blended, mixed family would be well received. It was just easier to stay away and figure it out on her own.

Then loss hit home again, her aunt had been diagnosed with cancer and she fought the good fight. She fought for years, going into remission, back out of remission and back again. She eventually lost her battle as well. Leaving behind a family devastated by her loss. She was the life and heart and soul of family gatherings. Her loss was felt by all.

It was not all bad in Anna's childhood. There were good times too. There were the annual trips to visit her grandparents in Florida. The vacations to New Hampshire and New York. There were the happy times and fond memories of birthday parties and the holidays. There were family dinners, productive conversations and times with friends. She had her church family and friends and enjoyed going to Sunday school, where she would continue to nurture and foster her relationship with God and Jesus. She always felt so drawn to her spiritual relationships, and, while the other kids were carrying on and playing around, she was always seeking connection, deeper meaning and understanding.

Anna would often go out and play with her neighbors for hours on end. They would build tree forts and go four-wheeling through the woods and fields in their neighborhood. The snow days, where they would go out and sled for hours. She would fly her kites for hours looking up at the sky and enjoying the sight of the fluffy clouds. Many times, she would lay in the fields and look up at the sky and wonder what was up there. It was her escape. Nature provided such a place of calm and peace in her heart and mind.

THE CONNECTION FROM PAST TO PRESENT DAY

When Anna reflected on all of these things, she realized that her present marriage was a conglomeration of all of the unhealthy, toxic and abusive behaviors she experienced and feelings she felt as a kid. Lionel was a complete representation of her father, mother, grandfather and the men she had dated and the one she had experienced in her first marriage. Because she had grown up in such a toxic family dynamic plagued with generational trauma, this relationship felt like home. Of course, she did not recognize this until she was several years in and then out the door, but it all started to make sense.

He represented her father in the sense that she felt like she was never good enough and was always tossed aside for others, unless she had something to offer at the time. She realized that if she could just create value, she could get her father's attention. Knowing that he had remarried and had another daughter, she always felt like she was in second place. This constant fight for love and attention was a constant struggle for Anna. Her relationship with Lionel mimicked this exact behavior.

When it came to business and the need for success, power and money, it felt very similar to her experience with her mother. Her mother was a high-powered successful business owner, who took the fax machine on vacation. Business always came first. Anna distinctly remembers being pulled out of the bridal suite, while getting into her wedding dress on her wedding day to collect a payment that had been outstanding for a large contract. She even expressed to Lionel that she felt it could wait, as she was literally surrounded by make-up and hair stylists and a team of her best girlfriends helping her get into her wedding dress, when she was politely told that business always comes first. That was the moment of clarity, where she knew that she had signed up for more than she had bargained for, and her feelings and special moments were not a priority.

Then, there was the distinct connection between the behaviors of her grandfather and Lionel. Her grandfather was constantly commenting on Anna's weight, eating habits and appearance. It was unnerving and always made her feel self-conscious. This began the lifelong self-esteem challenges that she faced no matter how many times others told her she was beautiful. She did not believe it because she always heard the little voices and comments from childhood that plagued her. Lionel played this role perfectly.

He would constantly criticize her, comment on her weight, select her clothing and remark that she needed to wear more fitted clothing to make her look smaller, take her to the gym and insist that she complete his workouts. Interestingly enough, this did not stop him from constantly taking her out to eat and indulging in food options that were not exactly the healthiest for weight control.

Anna distinctly remembers going out for Valentine's Day and at the end of the meal ordering a shareable dessert, which she never did, as she typically was not a dessert fan. The next day, he publicly humiliated her, by chastising her for eating half of the piece of cake, in front of her family, and indicated that if she really cared about her weight, she would have only eaten the fruit on the top of the cake, not the cake itself. This was no different than the year he bought her a red velvet cake for her birthday and then gave her a lecture about why she should not eat cake. After that speech, she did not even bother with having a celebration and singing, she simply threw the entire cake in the garbage and decided to forgo her birthday celebration. This felt very familiar, as her grandfather used to take the family to buffets for dinner, when she would visit her father and tell the kids to clean their plates, it was rude and disrespectful if you did not because children in the world were starving. He would then, after over feeding everyone, pick on Anna for "being fat" when she weighed all of one hundred and twenty pounds. Again, the feelings from those childhood experiences were mirrored and reinforced in her relationship with Lionel.

Lionel expected Anna to be available at his beckon call and be there to serve him as if she was his servant. He had no regard for her sleep, health or needs. Lionel would make comments to her like "this is the difference between a girlfriend and a wife" and literally complain about having intimate relations on his terms. He would go out until two or three am and come home when she was asleep and be upset that she was not awake and dressed in her finest lingerie. However, when she was in the mood for some love and affection, he would find ways to dismiss her. It was almost as if he was using her needs as a control mechanism. She was puzzled by this behavior. She felt unattractive and only worth his time when he was in the mood. Again, a familiar feeling from childhood of always waiting for love and affection.

As Anna began to connect the dots, she realized she needed to look further into her past and decided to assess her first marriage. She had been married previously to Frank for almost fourteen years. This marriage resulted in them having children together and was one that began when she was very young. She had gone to college and fell in love with a much older man. At the time, it seemed so exciting because he was older, and she was the young hot momma. He wooed her and promised her the world and as naïve as she was, she fell for all of it. It was not until after she was married, and pregnant with her first child that the true character of the man she married was revealed. He became very controlling, drank and smoked constantly. There were several instances that turned physically violent, and she was not sure what to do. At this time, her family was barely speaking to her, as there had been some falling outs as she chose to marry a man that they were not in agreement with.

She did not quite realize what she had gotten herself into, but because she was a good "Catholic girl," she felt that she had to honor her promise she made to God on the day she was wed. However, over time, and as the family grew, the relationship became more and more toxic and intolerable. She recalls feeling so sad inside, so unloved and so lonely. Her life had turned into a vicious cycle of wash, rinse and repeat every single day. Just trying to go through the motions, not knowing if she was going to get a lecture, be yelled at for not doing things the way he wanted them done or if he was going to come home drunk or high and lose his cool on her or the kids. Anna recalls being thrown in a closet one night when he was angry after coming home from a night of drinking. After he finished throwing her in the closet and spitting all over her as he yelled in her face, he threw her out of the house in the middle of the night with nothing more than her car key. He had taken her phone, she was in her pajamas and had no purse, wallet, or ID. She was left to fend for herself at a pay phone to call for help as her six-month old baby was inside the house unattended with her drunk husband. This lifestyle left Anna feeling like she was walking on eggshells constantly.

Another relationship of impossible unattainable expectations. She was never enough, never good enough and he too had a wandering eye. Despite his daily demand for intimacy, she felt like she was never good enough, never pretty enough to keep his full attention. As her body changed, baby after baby she felt more and more self-conscious and slowly began to feel the overwhelming feelings of childhood creep in about her weight and figure. The result, endless hours of exercise and distorted perceptions of herself. The constant critiques she received once again felt like a blend of familiar behaviors from her childhood received from both her maternal and paternal sides of her family. A battle and inner conflict that continued from her early years of life...again...very familiar and very unhealthy!

PART THREE

A QUEST FOR DISCOVERING THE TRUTH

Anna's story is a story of a woman's life interrupted. A life that had strayed many times from the path that she was meant to live. A life that had been tempted, tried and led astray by the various situations and circumstances presented to her as she blindly and aimlessly walked through life. Anna's story contains unique, personal, firsthand accounts of specific memories and circumstances, but there are many similar stories that exist throughout the human experience over time. Every human being has a story, and each story tells the tale of how and why a person behaves and reacts the way they do. This blueprint becomes an operating system that is created and captures the various limiting beliefs that have developed and unfolded throughout a person's life. What is not unique to Anna's story is that we all have one thing in common...WE are all trying to figure out the secret to SURVIVING THE HUMAN EXPERIENCE.

This section of the book will explore the various lessons, tools and quest for discovering the TRUTH that occur as one continues to grow and evolve through life's experiences. This section of the book takes the reader on a journey...a journey of discovery and exploration aimed at finding one's own personal truth! A journey solely focused on bringing a message of hope, healing and a very strong, clear message to share with fellow humans that...IT IS TIME TO WAKE UP!!!

WAKE UP!!!

Yes...that's right...I said it...IT'S TIME TO WAKE UP!!! Being in human form and on this Earth is a gift. A God-given opportunity and gift to experience life in human form to explore and seek out fulfilling moments. It is not a gift to be thrown away or led astray. Each and every person's time on Earth is short, compared to the time of the eternal soul experience. So, if we know life is short...why do we continue to live unconscious...asleep?!? Why do we continue to GIVE AWAY OUR POWER to others who do not see our value and do not honor and cherish our gifts? Why do we fall victim to temptations? Why do we look the other way despite the unease in the pit of our stomach, the red flags and the bad vibes we feel from interactions with others? Why do we seek outside validation? Why do we not TRUST OUR OWN INTUITION? Why...why...why? This list could go on and on, but you get the point of where I am going.

IT ALL STOPS NOW...TODAY...NOT EVER AGAIN...IT IS TIME TO WAKE UP AND RECLAIM YOUR GOD-GIVEN BIRTH RIGHT OF TRANSCINDENTAL AUTHORITY AND RECLAIM YOUR POWER!!!

THE LESSONS

Over time Anna's curiosity continued to grow as she continued to explore spirituality and make sense of this new way of living, thinking and processing all of the new knowledge she was gaining. It was as if she was learning, unlearning and re-learning her human experience. She found herself, in quiet moments, coming up with questions to explore. When she would go for her sessions, she would show up with her notebook in hand and have a series of questions ready to discuss. It was as if she could not learn fast enough, and she was so thirsty for answers...a seeker of understanding and knowledge...on a quest to uncover THE TRUTH...HER TRUTH.

The reality was...the only one who could help her discover the truth was herself and God. The guides who had been placed in her life along the way were just that ... guides... they were there to aid and assist her, but it was Anna who needed to do the work. She was the only one who could lead herself to the answer. It was through her relationship and conversations with God that this would be done.

At this point in her journey, Anna had come to a fork in the road, she had two options, she could either choose to continue down the path of self-destruction that she was on, or she could choose to re-create the life that was supposed to be her journey and live out her remaining time on Earth living her purpose. The choice was hers, and God was waiting for her to make the decision. Free will is one of the many great gifts our maker has given each of us and, one must always remember, we get to make our choices. Of course, every choice comes with consequences. Those consequences can be positive or negative, but, ultimately, the path we take is our own personal responsibility.

It was during this phase of Anna's journey that she began to realize the many lessons she had learned throughout her time on Earth. There were many and each one was important to her spiritual growth and healing process. Some were more pleasant than others, but when she quieted her mind, did the work and sat with herself, she could see the true blessings that these lessons delivered. Here are just a few of the most profound for her.

She learned...

TRUSTING GOD is key, even when you are not sure what is happening. God hears conversations and sees actions that sometimes we are not privy to, and he is there ready to protect us against what we may not be able to see. For this reason, sometimes decisions we do not understand are designed to protect us. We get so caught up in being upset that things do not turn out the way we want that we miss the blessing in all that did not play out the way we had hoped. Often times, it is because there is something bigger and better waiting for us. If we just have FAITH and get to the other side of what we are experiencing, we can see the true beauty in what lies ahead.

YOUR relationship with GOD is YOUR relationship with GOD! This is a profound statement. In today's world there are so many people out there trying to interpret, share or tell YOU what God says about life, your life or what you should be doing in the name of God. This can be seen all throughout society, religion and many other spaces, in reality, your relationship with God is personal. As a result, you do not need an intermediary to have a conversation with God. You have the direct connection to talk to God whenever you so choose. You can do so formally or informally, in prayer or in casual conversation.

A phenomenal series of books Anna read along her journey were written by Neal Donald Walsch, *Conversations with God*. In the books, the author shares his conversations he had with God in an open dialogue format. The conversations and information shared in these books were very enlightening. There were so many topics and conversations shared.

The reality is we are all Children of God. Some may not have chosen to accept this relationship, but the reality is, God is there ready, willing and able when you are ready to embrace the love and relationship that awaits. God is waiting patiently through his unconditional divine love to bring all of his children back home. It is interesting how so many of us spend so much time in life searching for and seeking connection with God. God is in each and every one of us. We have all been made in the image and likeness of God to be co-creators. All you have to do is start the conversation!

Anna survived her life experiences. Although *she is not responsible for the things that happened to her, SHE IS RESPONSIBLE FOR HEALING HERSELF.* Anna may not have intentionally asked for what had been dealt to her, but despite the pain and hardships, she worked through lessons, reasons and life experiences that changed who she became. The result of this conglomeration of experiences resulted in some deep wounds and scars. It was no one's job to explore and heal those wounds for her. She had to do the work and she had to heal herself and make herself whole again...as Anna was the only one who had the POWER to do it!

The most important relationship you will ever have will be the relationship with YOURSELF. No one can truly understand YOU like YOU understand YOURSELF. For this reason, you must do the work to explore and fully understand yourself...the light and the dark. Figuring out what makes you tick should be YOUR NUMBER ONE PRIORITY!

The quality of the relationship you have with YOURSELF will lay the foundation for the quality of the relationships you have with others and the treatment you receive. If you do not take time for yourself, love yourself first and constantly put others above you, you will send out the vibration to the world that you value others more than yourself. That...is dangerous, because that positions you and opens you up to be taken advantage of and used. There is nothing a "taker" loves more than a person who is a "giver." "Takers" continue to take without regard for your well-being.

We all have our own POWER and YOU SHOULD NEVER GIVE THAT AWAY TO ANYONE. Your power is yours and yours only. It is unique and specific to you. Honoring and respecting your power is key. When you finally understand who you are, why you are here and the power that is your human right...you will not engage in experiences and/or with others that compromise YOU!

SEEKING VALIDATION FROM OTHERS IS NOT NECESSARY. You have what you need within yourself. Seeking validation from outside of yourself is a sure way to set yourself up for disappointment and creates relationships based on co-dependence. Asking for opinions is okay, but feeling the need to receive validation from others to make decisions is not healthy for your mind, body or soul. You have to be comfortable with making your own decisions and be true to yourself. Getting or seeking the approval of others diminishes your trust and confidence in yourself.

When people show you who they are, believe them! Do not allow someone to do something that does not sit right with your spirit, and just keep going like nothing happened. If someone shows you who they are for the first time, then believe them. There were so many times that Anna wanted to only see the good and would dismiss the "not so good" that it ended up costing her so much of her time, energy and happiness. She would sit in discomfort, while others would literally be living their best life, while taking advantage of her. She wanted so badly to only see the good, but reality is reality is if someone tells you who they are...then you should believe them!

Pay attention to the red flags! When they show up, pay attention the first time. Continuing to analyze, question and justify why certain things may be taking place, happening or being said is not necessary. If something does not seem right, feel right or look right, then that is it. Anna would try to rationalize or take the blame for many situations and/or circumstances she experienced because she was not certain about what was happening. After watching this replay several times, she decided that enough was enough and if she saw a red flag, which one was it. No need for further discovery or conversation. Yes...in taking this approach, sometimes you may leave behind someone or something that may have been mistaken in interpretation, but at this stage of the game, she could no longer afford to keep giving others the benefit of the doubt. She had been through enough and did not have the time or tolerance to put herself in positions where people could talk down to, mistreat or dismiss her. If the individuals coming into her life were not here for a healthy purpose, there was no space for a relationship or interaction.

If it does not feel right...WALK AWAY! Learning how to gauge emotions as an indicator of the effects of others energy is placed on you, this is a skill to be learned. If emotions are being experienced that let you know a situation does not feel right...no need to second guess. Listen to that gut instinct feeling, appreciate your intuition and move on.

Never sacrifice your peace for someone else's comfort! There is nothing on this planet that is worth sacrificing your own peace! Anna had come too far and worked too hard to allow anything or anyone in her space that threatened her sense of self, peace of mind or inner peace. Putting your feelings aside at someone else's expense never ends well for YOU! YOU are the MOST IMPORTANT PERSON in YOUR life!

EVERYONE THAT CLAIMS TO BE YOUR FRIEND IS NOT ALWAYS YOUR FRIEND. Along the journey, Anna found that many of the people who had entered into her life were there for their own selfish needs. Being able to stand back and watch people's behaviors and observe actions told a much more accurate story than the words being said. It was through this lesson that Anna learned that trust cannot be given to those who do not earn it and that, often times, people are there for the benefit of what you have to offer, versus there with genuine intentions. She slowly began to take inventory of everyone in her life and noticed that when she pulled back and stopped offering and being such a giver that there were many who did not reach out until they needed something. She also was able to assess the behaviors of others when she was making progress in her own life. Several people who had been her "friend" suddenly disappeared or would diminish her moments of success. She quickly realized that if the ones who said they were "friends" could not rejoice and celebrate in her happy moments, they did not deserve a spot in her "friend" space.

PROTECT YOUR ENERGY. This was a big one. Not everyone enters your life with good intentions. Some come to see what they can get...others come to be part of the action or create drama. Energy can be given or taken and if you are an empath, the energy suckers will certainly seek you out. Anna learned this lesson the hard way...over and over until she finally figured it out and decided that this could not happen anymore. She began to slowly isolate herself and hibernate for a period of time. In order to restore her energy and learn techniques to block and protect her energy from others whose intentions were to benefit from feeding off of her energy.

YOU ARE NOT YOUR MIND. We may all have a mind, but it is not the essence of who you are...it is simply a tool that is given to you like a compass to use throughout your life. Being aware of and observing the thoughts in your mind are an essential part of your awareness of self and part of the awakening experience. Pattern interruption for thoughts that do not serve your greater good is a great tool to get started on breaking the cycle of getting lost in thought or becoming consumed with your thoughts.

Pay attention to actions and not words. Words can be said, but with the absence of action, words are empty. This could not have proved truer for Anna. She found herself regularly being gaslit whenever she was trying to voice her opinion. When she would speak, she would often be interrupted with the statement, "you have pretty eyes," and every time it would throw her off and she would lose her train of thought. Gaslighting and love bombing are real tactics that are used. Lots of empty promises and future fallacies would enter conversations. These tactics are used by people who use the talking with no action approach to getting what they want and using others. Words can awaken the emotion and feelings of hope inside, but they should never be used as the sole assessment of how a person treats you, because the PROOF IS IN THE ACTION, NOT THE WORDS! Not everyone is meant to stay. Some people come into our lives for a season and a reason, then when their purpose has been served, it is important to be grateful for the time and/or lessons learned, cherish that time and move forward.

YOU do not have to be a recipient of that hurt nor are you responsible for fixing anyone's unhealed wounds. YOU are responsible for YOURSELF and YOUR HEALING. YOU can lead a horse to water, but you cannot force the horse to drink. So, remaining in an abusive situation with the hopes of healing another and being a martyr, is not YOUR job.

When you cannot change what is happening around you...YOU can always decide how YOU choose to respond. There are a lot of personalities and behaviors that will be encountered throughout your lifetime, and some will be pleasant while others not so much. For this reason, it is necessary to learn how to monitor, observe and manage your responses to external factors and stimuli that could potentially impact your reactions. Being aware of triggers and what sends you from zero to one hundred is the first step in becoming aware of what affects your internal responses. Once you have identified these hot button behaviors, you can implement tools and skills to deploy when faced with these situations. Once you have mastered your emotional responses and implemented safeguards you can manage and own your peace always!

The only one responsible for YOUR HAPPINENESS IS YOU! If you are looking for happiness from someone else, that is the WRONG ANSWER. HAPPINESS COMES FROM WITHIN and not from anyone or any external factor. IT IS NO ONE'S JOB OR RESPONSIBILTY TO MAKE YOU HAPPY! That kind of pressure and expectation is not only unrealistic, but an unfair demand on another. Until you have found happiness, peace and enjoyment within yourself, you will not master the art of happiness. FIND YOUR OWN HAPPY BEFORE YOU BRING ANOTHER HUMAN BEING INTO YOUR PERSONAL REALM!

Life is about pain and passion! Yes, there is a spectrum of emotions to be felt throughout each personal experience, however, there are two prominent central themes throughout life and life events. These two themes are PAIN and PASSION. If an experience is not invoking a sense or experience filled with passion, it is likely bringing you pain. Pain brings lessons if you are able to sit still long enough to learn the lessons. Passion invokes a sense of purpose and fulfillment. In an ideal world, the goal would be to experience more passion than pain, but everyone's journey is different, and they are typically filled with a combination of both.

Pay attention to how others make you feel! If you notice that others are talking down to you, criticizing you or even trying to act as if they are better than you...immediately walk away. The world is cruel enough and allowing negativity into your space is a choice. YOU DESERVE NOTHING BUT LOVE, SUPPORT AND HEALTHY INTERACTIONS IN YOUR PERSONAL SPACE. If someone finds the need to belittle you in any way, they have to go. Anna experienced this firsthand in a variety of relationships and settings in her life, to include romantic relationships, friendships and work settings. As she began to redefine what was and what was not acceptable to her in her own personal space, she noticed that God quickly began removing people and revealing who they truly were right before her eyes.

YOU ONLY GET ONE BODY…TAKE CARE OF IT! When we arrive on this earth, we are given one body to carry us through our entire human experience. Throughout your experience it is YOUR JOB TO TAKE CARE OF YOUR BODY! Every decision you make during your human experience impacts your physical body, so choose wisely! Anna recalled hearing her mother tell her as a child, "you only get one body," and at the time she did not take her seriously. The reality is…if you were given a car and told you only get one car for your entire life on Earth…do you think you would take better care of it? The answer is probably yes. So, why should your body be any different? Many have said that in your early years of life you spend your time chasing wealth and when you are older you spend your wealth chasing your health. So, if we stopped to take the time to care for this beautiful human form earlier in life, it is quite possible that many health-related situations could be avoided.

SURVIVING THE HUMAN EXPERIENCE

The human experience is filled with complexities, and often more questions than answers. There is no instruction manual that is given when you begin your life on Earth. Earth school is not a thing, although it would be quite helpful! You arrive and are delivered to your parents, who are charged with the responsibility of raising you. In some instances, it is not the biological parents that provide the human experience, known as upbringing or raising the child. There are grandparents, legal guardians, aunts and uncles, family friends, foster parents and so many other options for the upbringing and care of a child. The quality of the experience of a child's early years is often determined by the experience of those who are charged with raising the child. If the responsible parties are loving, kind, caring and good citizens...then you have a shot at having a fairly normal and healthy household experience, but, then again, what is considered "normal" nowadays? If the environment is one where abuse, alcoholism, violence, drugs or gambling addictions are present...then the experience is going to be quite different. It is during the upbringing time period that a child will form most of their belief systems around love, relationships, interactions with the world, and general thoughts and ideas about life. For this reason, quality of upbringing can make or break a person's belief system and be the main driver of a framework of limiting beliefs.

Then, there are the formative middle school years. Ah yes...here is where friend groups matter, and peer pressure begins to set in. No longer is it your household structure and interactions that drive your thoughts, but now comes the introduction of peer pressure. Fitting in becomes a big deal. Puberty begins setting in, and all of a sudden you go from being completely dependent on those charged with your upbringing to now beginning to test your sea legs in the realm of independence. This is quite an awkward stage. You are not quite grown, but you start thinking you have some power. The quality of exposure to peer groups, activities, environment and your ability to be accepted by those you are around becomes a big deal. Here we go again...another opportunity to develop limiting beliefs. For example, if you experience a traumatic experience surrounding your peers like getting bullied, not fitting in, not wearing the right clothes, not being liked, not being part of the popular crew, these events may create an opportunity for limiting beliefs to transpire and manifest as fear, doubt, diminished self-confidence, low self-esteem, worthiness, etc.

Next up...the teen years. Oh yes...this is where it gets even trickier! During this time, peers really play a front and center role. The quality of information being fed into the brain by friends, social media sites, TV shows and series, movies and all other external influences have a profound effect on impressionable minds. During this period of time, so many things begin occurring and freedom is much more at the center of a teen's life than it had been in earlier years. These are the years where driver's licenses become a thing. Teens are starting to venture out on their own, parties start happening that go beyond the middle school birthday party setting, activities at school go from the "everyone gets a trophy" concept to performance determines college scholarships, and romantic relationships become a thing. Many caregivers/child raisers begin to become a little more hands off and often times the majority of a child's thoughts and ideas about the world have been formed by this stage of life and are being reinforced with the behaviors that are being displayed.

Then, if you have survived the teen years…it is time to join the adult world and either go to work, the military, college or travel the world. No longer are you living fancy free at someone else's expense. This is when things get real! Life smacks you in the face, whether you are ready or not. If you choose to go to college and live on campus you may get to stretch some of that transition out a little longer. If not, you are jumping right into the world…ready or not…here you come. All of a sudden bills become a real thing. A job is a necessity not a nicety. Those who were charged with your upbringing have either deemed you a success or a failure, based on "how you turned out." Relationships become a lot more complicated, both romantic and friendships.

The fun continues…adulthood has arrived. This is the period of time that responsibility, accountability and putting all of your upbringing training into action becomes real. Now you get to put everything you have learned into action…your philosophy about life, your character, morals, values, religious beliefs, spiritual beliefs, limiting beliefs and ideas about how the world works.

Many will start careers, get involved in serious relationships, get married, get pets, have children, accumulate debt, get a job, start a business, travel the world...the list goes on and on. During all of these years...your childhood traumas, limiting beliefs, religious beliefs, spiritual beliefs, financial beliefs, positive experiences, child raising beliefs, work ethic, and anything else you picked up along the way, will show up in expected and unexpected ways. The positives will play out and you will see them develop into what will be areas of strength for you. The "not so positive" will play out and in some cases become your weaknesses. Relationships will thrive or fold...some will result in marriage...some divorce. Children may enter the picture or sometimes just pets. Everything is dependent upon the belief system and wants and desires of the individuals in the relationship. There are so many variables and factors that unfold.

The real dilemma throughout this entire process is figuring out how to survive the human experience, despite all of the obstacles and challenges that life may throw at you. It all begins when the soul touches down on Earth and the decision is made to begin the human experience through birth. Once the journey begins, it truly is a matter of how the soul's human experience will unfold. Looking at the environment and experiences that occur as well as the level of AWAKENING the human experiences throughout life. If the soul's purpose is sidetracked or interrupted while going through the human experience, it is up to the individual to decide if getting back on course is the desired action or if the soul will not complete its intended purpose while here on Earth.

THE HUMAN EXPERIENCE

What does that even mean? What is the human experience? Is there a purpose? If so, how do you find the purpose? This has been one of the most explored questions ever as humans continue to walk this Earth and ask themselves the same basic questions. Who am I? What is My Purpose? Does My Life Matter? So, if everyone is faced with asking the same basic questions throughout their life, why have the answers not been more readily available? Have these questions been answered? Is it really that complicated?

Apparently, it is more complicated than any of us all thought, because the answers do not lie in the human realm. It is so much bigger, so much deeper and so much clearer when it is all put into perspective. Putting it into perspective and taking the journey through enlightenment by AWAKENING, brings all of the answers to light. The journey of creation provides so many answers to the questions every human asks at some point in their life. Now, on to explore some of these questions.

WHO AM I?

That is the million-dollar question. People spend a lifetime asking this question and seeking the answer. Some reply with the roles they play...a spouse, parent, job title or a dream fulfilled or unfulfilled. Others simply say, "I am still trying to find myself." Many spend thousands and thousands of dollars going to therapists, churches, hiring coaches and so many other methods only to find out, in the end, that the only person who has that answer is the person asking the question and God himself.

The answer is really quite simple, when the complicated human thought dynamics are removed. Anna had to ask all of these questions and through many readings, teachings and much self-discovery was able to conclude a very simple answer...she was a soul having a human experience. That is who she was. A Soul having a human experience. Not only was she a soul having a human experience...but, she was here with a purpose.

It was during this part of Anna's journey that she found profound teachings through reading Gary Zukav's, *Seat of the Soul* and Michael Singer's *The Untethered Soul*. Both of these books explored the soul and human experience on such a deep level that incorporated spirituality and life experiences. The messages were so clear and necessary for assisting Anna in answering the question she was exploring about who she was.

PURPOSE VERSUS VALUE

Another interesting thing to explore is, what is the difference between purpose and value? At first, when Anna explored this question, she thought...well if something has value then it must have purpose. Sounded pretty logical...until she explored this question with the concept of energy added to the equation. In reality...they mean very different things, although they can be intertwined. One of the readings that helped Anna to unpack this topic was *Woman Evolve*, by Sarah Jakes Roberts. In this book, Roberts really awakens the inner self and calls to action the need to evolve, which ultimately makes the reader call into question the areas of purpose and value. The lessons in this book were absolutely priceless.

Purpose

Just because something has purpose, does not mean that it has value for YOU or where YOU are in your life. There are plenty of things that have purpose in life, but may not be applicable for YOU in the time and space that you are in.

Value

The only person that determines your value is "YOU." YOU have the POWER to determine and assess your own value. No one else determines your worth, but YOU!

Anna had heard this her whole life and honestly, she really had not put much thought into it, because she always just went through life without really putting much effort and thought into her value. She really began to dive into this topic when she read the book, *Believe It*, by Jamie Kern Lima. This book taught her that when everyone around you does not believe in you, you need to keep going anyway. Never give up on your dreams or yourself because you have value! She followed this up with *Radical Confidence* by Lisa Bilyeu. Bilyeu's writing focused on her experience of creating the confidence that, ultimately, results in seeing, accepting and being proud of your own value. There were so many key takeaways in this book, as Anna began to restore her confidence while finding and reconnecting with her true self.

WHAT IS MY PURPOSE?

This is one of the most asked questions as life unfolds. The purpose is a God-given purpose. Before arriving on Earth, the soul was given a mission to accomplish. The soul knows its purpose, but the human body, which the soul occupies, is not always in alignment with its soul. When this happens, it can cause distractions or the individual to veer off course. It can be temporary and lesson after lesson is delivered to bring the body and soul back into alignment. For those who are less in tune, there may be a complete disconnect or the mission may not be fully completed. If this is the case, often times, the human experience will be one that is considered to be unfulfilled.

For years and years, Anna thought her purpose was the role she was playing for each time period in her life. Initially, it was to be the best daughter she could be. Then, it was to be the best student she could be during her early education years. When friendships became important in the development stages, she focused on being the best friend she could be to those who were in her circle. Romantic relationships became front and center during her teen years and yes...you guessed it...she was determined to be the best girlfriend a guy could ask for. Everyone had always joked that she was not the girlfriend type...she was the wife type, and this could not have been truer. As life continued, she adapted to be the best whatever she could be for whatever phase of life she was in...best wife...best mother...best employee, etc.

No wonder she could not figure out HER PURPOSE!!! Anna was so busy trying to be so adaptable and flexible for everyone around her that SHE NEVER PUT HERSELF FIRST or asked HERSELF WHAT HER PURPOSE WAS!!!

She spent years and years exploring things she liked, passions, hobbies and asking others what they thought her purpose was as if they knew her better than she knew herself. Vision board after vision board...resolutions, goals, road maps and more and still no answer. Until she finally asked the question..." God... what is my purpose?" She had to sit with herself silently and wait until all was still and then she heard the words loud and clear..."TO SERVE." She looked around and saw no one in the room with her and asked yet again...what is my purpose and got the same response..."TO SERVE." It was at that moment that she realized that the purpose in human form is to serve. Serving could be a variety of things and have many meanings to others. For Anna, she instantly knew that it meant to serve in whatever capacity she was called to serve. She became overwhelmed with emotion and excitement as all this time she had been overcomplicating things, expecting some very definitive answer and, in the end, it was so much broader and more impactful than she ever imagined.

She began to reflect on how many bizarre experiences she had been through throughout her life and there was no rhyme or reason to any of them. The only common theme in all of the unrelated events was that she was called to serve in ways that expressed compassion, empathy, action without thought and being available to serve in whatever capacity the situation required. She would do so over and over again and never quite understand what was happening or why it was happening. Then she realized that throughout all of the life events and moments, she was called to be an Earth Angel...emitting love and providing light to others as times became dark and events tested the individual(s) human experience and humanity at large.

Her purpose was much greater than she had ever realized and that brought about a feeling of honor and gratefulness all at once. Thank you...thank you for choosing me to be able to bring light to others, to express love and compassion, regardless of any situation or trial and tribulation she faced. All the searching and all the complicated exercises to figure out her purpose and, literally, all she had to do was ask.

DOES MY LIFE MATTER?

Everyone wants to feel important, special, loved and a part of something bigger than themselves. This is where fear, doubt, shame, guilt, lack of confidence, diminishing self-esteem and all things built to tear a person down creep in. Everyone was brought into the human experience to create and experience life in a physical form. For that reason alone, YES, every life matters. Every human plays a role in the collective "oneness" that exists. It is like a symphony orchestra. Everyone has their part in the collective experience. Everyone's role is different in the musical piece, but when played together the results are extraordinary and result in harmony. When the musicians are out of sync, the musical piece is imbalanced and does not flow and the coherent harmonious musical piece is out of whack. Some may appear to be more profound (by human definition) than others, but no human experience is less valuable than another. So, the answer is...YES, EVERY LIFE MATTERS!

For Anna, this was confirmed every day that she would wake up and see the sun. She knew that God would continue to see her value and is saying that her work here is not done. The mere fact that she was awake and alive, meant she still had a mission to complete. She was constantly reminded throughout the day that her life does matter by the wonderful opportunities she is given each and every day. Sometimes they are more exciting than others, but the reality is, every experience offers something great if you look for the silver lining. She also was reminded of how much her life matters by the family, friends, coworkers and other fellow brothers and sisters she would come into contact with daily. On the days that her human form struggles with this concept of mattering, she would look at her children and know that she is loved, cherished, appreciated and that she matters. God has blessed her with them, and they are her constant reminder that her life has purpose and meaning.

WHAT DOES THIS ALL MEAN?

So, if we are all souls having a human experience, what is this really all about? The reality is the human experience is a form of the matrix, one where the individual players in the game are creating human experiences as they go through thought, energetic vibrations, intentions, manifestations and simply putting ideas into the universe. Sometimes these combinations are from the individual and sometimes they come from the larger group known as the collective consciousness. This explains so many historical events, time periods and movements throughout the times. Anna was able to deep dive into this topic when reading the book, *The Vortex*, by Esther Hicks and Jerry Hicks.

The body is comprised of energy and conducts itself similar to the energy currents that flow through electricity. This makes humans energetic beings subject to the laws of attraction and the laws of the universe, which means humans have the power to create their own reality and experiences. How is this done?

It is done through thought. There are so many variations of the saying that if you can think it, it is possible. Well, that is very true. Most inventions began with an "out of the box" thought and then one day became reality. For example, the light bulb, computers, cell phones, electric cars and so much more! Another really great read that Anna studied during her discovery process was, *The Law of Attraction*, by Esther and Jerry Hicks.

Desirable outcomes require a person to change the thoughts that are being generated from the mind. How does one do this? It is a process that is not as simple as it sounds, but the answer is to gain control of the mind and quiet it. Once the mind no longer controls the body, the body is free to create more desirable experiences and explore endless opportunities. Doing this requires the human to shift from being a participant in the game to becoming the orchestrator of the game. A really great tool Anna adopted to assist with interrupting thoughts that are not productive, is to implement a strategy that was presented by Mel Robbins, in her book, *The High Five Habit*, where she shares that when negative thoughts or self-talk begin to creep in, you simply stop them by using a phrase to pattern interrupt. This really cool trick stops you dead in your tracks and requires you to immediately stop thinking whatever that thought was and move on to something more productive. Anna tried it several times and she absolutely loved a good pattern interruption! Pattern interruption methods change course almost instantly and allow you to reset your mind and move in a different direction or pattern of thought.

THE BODY IS NOT THE MIND!

For far too long the human brain has controlled the mind, body and spirit. But why? Why is this happening? Why do our thoughts consume our being? It is true that what you focus on, you will create. What consumes your thoughts will eventually consume your mind and that is the start to the downward spiral.

If you have negative thoughts, typically developed as a result of your unconscious limiting beliefs, and you continue to grow those thoughts and allow them to go unchallenged, you will eventually bring those thoughts forth to your reality. Allowing your thoughts and mind to continue to dwell in negative thoughts, emotions and feelings will eventually create space for an unhealthy experience that could eventually perpetuate into illness, mental illness, diminished health and analysis paralysis. This also lowers your energetic vibration, creating space to bring all of the undesired thoughts into your realm, as you may not be asking for the unpleasant thoughts to become a reality, but your unconscious does not recognize the difference and just recognizes that you are sending out a frequency that invites whatever it is you are thinking about into your space. Replacing those thoughts with happy thoughts changes the direction and quality of experiences. Moving towards healthier and positive desires will change your frequency and vibration, and that shift alone will begin to upgrade the quality of your experiences.

Anna remembers entering several relationships, unsure of her ability to trust the other to remain in a faithful, committed relationship. She was plagued with self-doubt. Would she be enough? Could she be enough for the person? She would buy all kinds of clothes, try all types of creative things to keep things "spicy," make herself available as often and on the terms of the other person's desires. Despite her constant thought of trying to please her partner, there was always this fear in the back of her mind, that there would be infidelity at some point. When she unpacked this, she realized that her very first serious romantic relationship of several years had resulted in cheating, and not just with one or two people, but with many. It was because of this experience that she carried this limiting belief into her relationships going forward. Consequently, she never thought she would be enough for any partner and despite her best efforts, the result was always the same outcome. She would attract the cheaters; she would listen to the sweet nothings whispered in her ear that they were faithful and would never cheat, that she had nothing to worry about and that she was the only one AND that was true...until reality set in and it was not.

Over and over again this story played out the same and it was not just "an affair," she attracted men who could probably be identified as sex addicts, who were just really good at playing the game and trying to play it off for the purpose of preserving their public image. Sometimes she wondered, had she not had that fear in the back of my mind, would the outcome have been different. Anna often thought, that if that was not a limiting belief that she had allowed to go unchecked, that she would not have entertained, attracted or dismissed the red flags from these type of men in the first place. More than likely, she would not have entertained, attracted or dismissed herself in that compromising position to begin with. As she came to realize through the AWAKENING pro-cess...looking back, she was not regretful of these experiences, because they were part of her story. She now knew that she did have the power at any time to change her vibration and frequency and attract healthier partners. Looking back now, she realized that had she healed her wounds and scars, she never would have even been interested in the type of men she became entangled with in her romantic space, because they could never have matched her power or energy had she been whole when she was seeking a relationship. The tricky part is...if you are not aware of any of the information, Anna was learning about on her journey, you would not know what that even looks like or where to begin.

Not to digress...back to the topic at hand...the body is not the mind!

So, if the body is not the mind and the mind is not the body, then what the heck is the purpose of thought? It seems as if it is almost more of a distraction than an aid. If that is the case, then is there a way to change it? Is it possible to quiet or silence the mind? Yes, there sure is a way to sit with yourself without allowing thoughts to consume your every movement and every moment. During this time of stillness is when you have the power to hack your brain and override your hardwired desire to control everything in your existence through thought alone. Through sitting quietly, meditating or simply allowing your mind to go blank, you have the opportunity to bridge the gap between your conscious and your subconscious. This is the opportunity to allow for alignment between your body and your soul. This can result in what is often referred to as "remembering." Remembering who you are and why you are here. The body is a tool for you to use to conduct your purpose. The mind is also a tool, but you must be watchful of your mind to ensure it does not run the show completely. The mind needs time to rest and caring for the mind is extremely important.

The quality of your thoughts will certainly determine the quality of your life! If left unchecked and uncared for, you can put yourself in a precarious situation and experience many unpleasant and undesired results and that is not the intended goal of the human experience.

During Anna's journey she found Dr. Joe Dispenza's teachings to really take this concept and drill down deeply. She read, *Becoming Supernatural, You are the Placebo* and *Breaking the Habit of Being Yourself*. In addition, she would listen to his YouTube videos and meditations and absorb many of his philosophies and teachings about the mind, body, spirit and quantum world. His teachings and research were action packed and full of science and research to support his findings. It was through his teachings that Anna began to learn how to quiet and take control of her mind. Previously her mind was flooded with worrisome thoughts and "what ifs." Through his techniques, she was able to finally get a hold of herself and learn the art of relaxation and being present in the moment.

Eckart Tolle's teachings added to her knowledge base. *The Power of Now*, *The Journey into Yourself* and *Transcending the Ego*, also had a profound impact on Anna's journey. It was through Tolle's teachings that Anna was able to look at life through a different lens and begin to get a hold of her emotions by learning that most feelings of anxiety come from living in the past or the future. In doing that, it creates a triggered response in the body that makes the mind and body believe that it is reliving moments in present time. Learning how to live in the NOW was a very challenging task for Anna, but one that became a daily exercise for her as she began to move forward into finding out who she was and being thankful and grateful for all that she had been and was becoming.

LIMITING BELIEFS

Where do they come from? What are they? Why do they cause so much chaos and so much dysfunction in our lives? Limiting beliefs are formed, in most cases, without our awareness and knowledge. They are beliefs we form after having experiences that have resulted in a manner that may or may not have served us, but we formed an idea around an experience that later became part of our being. Limiting beliefs are just that...LIMITING. They stop us from creating and leave us in a space of re-creating or expecting past outcomes to happen as a result of similar experiences. They can be debilitating and cause such confusion internally, and to those who experience life with us, if they go unaddressed. Being aware of your limiting beliefs and identifying them is the first step to uncovering the layers of false belief that has settled within your human experience. Identifying, addressing and challenging those beliefs is what will free you from those beliefs. Also, having awareness of your limitations, based on a false belief system, allows for growth and evolution.

For example, in exploring Anna's adult relationships and watching them unfold in toxic and unhealthy ways, she could not help but begin to explore what had gone wrong on a much deeper level. After reading Raine Howard's book, *Addicted to Pain: Renew Your Mind & Heal Your Spirit from a Toxic Relationship in Thirty Days*, she was able to identify various experiences in her life and the limiting beliefs that resulted. The author walks you through an exercise to conduct a relationship audit, to do an honest evaluation of the relationships in your life so that you can objectively assess the quality of the experience. It was in doing this exercise that she had her "ah ha" moment! She came from a divorced, household where at a young age her parents divorced. Anna stayed with her mom and her dad left the home. Her mom remained a single mother until Anna went to college. Her father was in a serious relationship a few months after her parents split up. During this time, she had managed to form and accept that she was not worthy of a man's love. Since her father had left, why should she expect differently from any other man? He had moved on, had a new family, new daughter and she felt like the red-headed stepchild, who was never enough. This interpretation of what had happened in her life played out through the series of romantic relationships she had moving forward. They were all the same...did not matter the age, race, religion or upbringing of the men she got involved with...they all ended in either physical, psychological or emotional abuse, sexualizing her, treating her more like an object than a human being and eventually ending in disaster.

With each of these experiences, she internalized each one and just thought...if she could just try a little harder, maybe one of them would love her enough...maybe one of them would love her enough to be faithful. You see...it was her limiting belief that she could never be enough...never be good enough...never be pretty enough...never be skinny enough...never be sexy enough...that continued this vicious cycle of sick, twisted, toxic relationships. The truth was...**SHE WAS ALWAYS GOOD ENOUGH**...matter of fact...**SHE WAS MORE THAN ENOUGH FOR ALL OF IT!** It was her limiting beliefs that kept her stuck in a space of lowering her vibration and attracting lower vibrational men into her life. Basically, she was dimming her light and fitting the mold of what these low vibration men were looking for in a relationship.

The truth is Anna would never have been enough for any of them, because she did not belong there in the first place. She was not where she was meant to be, and God humored her, and she used free will to carry out HER PLAN versus GOD'S PLAN FOR HER. As the old saying goes, you cannot lay down with a dog with fleas and not expect to come up with fleas. So, it was not until she examined and acknowledged her limiting beliefs around relationships that she realized that she was lowering herself, compromising her character and reputation, and taking on projects versus finding a true partner, an equal, a person of honesty and integrity, who was looking for someone to grow with and create an amazing human experience with while on this Earth.

You see...Anna had focused so much on the dream of growing up, getting married, having kids and having the family that she wanted so desperately as a little girl, that she had not done the work to heal her wounds to set herself up for success to find her Prince Charming. Because of her unintentional negligence to do the work that she did not realize she needed to do, she compromised her own soul and those of her children. As she became aware of the patterns and what was happening, she decided to do the inner work. Anna made a commitment to herself to choose to be intentionally single and heal herself before engaging any further in romantic relationships. She did not give up on love, as she knew that God has the perfect person out there for her, but it is not until she addresses all of the wounds and scars around the romantic relationships that she had experienced during this journey on Earth that God will then reveal her life companion.

This is the part of the process where Anna had to take her limiting belief work a step further. She had to truly learn about and embrace the concept of forgiveness. This was a hard lesson for her, because the hurt, pain, betrayal, broken trust and the basic decency of her human value had been jeopardized so many times. It was hard to fathom forgiving the men who had deeply wounded her soul with no regard for her heart. It was not until she truly understood forgiveness that she found this to be the most rewarding lesson ever. Once Anna knew forgiveness was not for the other person, but for herself, she realized that it was a necessary step in the grieving process. Just because she had decided to exercise forgiveness did not mean she had to engage with the individuals who had harmed her. She could still love them, wish them well and choose to not allow herself to be in the space of an unhealthy situation. The relationships may not have worked, she had been blaming herself for something that was not 100 percent her fault, she was holding the blame for the entire experience, but it takes two and it was not her responsibility to shoulder the entire blame for things not working out. Once she learned how to forgive herself, she began to feel the true healing begin.

Anna also proceeded to further educate herself by reading the book, *Adult Children of Emotionally Immature Parents*, by Lindsay Gibson, PsyD, to learn the psychology behind parent/child relationships. Generational cycles of parenting and child rearing have been at the mercy of the parental/guardian's ability to execute the child raising roles. In some cases, the parents/guardians raising the child(ren) may have had experiences and traumas in their lives that affect their ability to connect with or effectively parent their child(ren). This book further explores and examines what happens in those instances and helped Anna to further understand the parent/child dynamics and the backstory of how limiting beliefs can manifest back to childhood.

WHAT DOES HEALING LOOK LIKE?

Through her journey, Anna learned that the healing process is not a linear one and it can be very messy. The truth is, there is no secret formula to follow that lays the foundation and the path for healing. Each person's scars, wounds and experiences are unique to that specific person. For this reason, different approaches and modalities are more impactful and practical for some more than others. For that reason, it is important to figure out what speaks to YOU and what feels right for YOU. The goal is to share some of the really useful information and healing tools and opportunities that worked for Anna as she continued to AWAKEN.

Truth and transparency...there were moments where Anna found herself sitting in a puddle of tears balled up not knowing what to do next. Then, there were moments when she felt overcome with anger, sadness, frustration and an overwhelming sense of grief. Because she had always been taught to suck it up and move on, she did not know how to handle these moments. It was such a foreign experience to her and to go through it alone without anyone to hold her or tell her it was going to be okay felt like a slow painful death. She literally wondered at several points in time, if she would ever smile or be happy again. The emptiness and loss were beyond any feeling she had ever imagined. The crazy part was, she could not decipher if it was the loss of the relationship or the loss of what she thought she had and what could have been. During these dark moments, it is hard to make rationale sense of the emotions that take over.

The stories just kept playing on repeat and all she could remember was the deep pain that cast over everything. It was during this time that she was able to seek the support, comfort and reassurance from her family, closest friend and her soul family. Without their support she was sure this process would have taken much longer. As she continued to call on the support of her loved ones, and took things one day at a time, she realized that this was not the end of her life, but the end of a very painful chapter that was full of lessons that had presented at the next level. You see...Anna distinctly remembered the words of a counselor after her first divorce where she shared that if Anna did not address the issues from the first marriage and the attraction of a narcissist, she would attract the same and re-create the same situation in a different form. At the time, Anna had no idea what that even meant. She had no idea what a narcissist was, nevertheless, how to not attract another one. Little did she know she would re-create the same situation immediately after leaving that relationship. Because she clearly was a little hard-headed, this experience turned out to be more extreme and almost cost her, her life. She could only imagine that God said...well...she does not learn easy, so we are going to have to make this an impactful lesson she will not forget. Message received! It still did not make it any easier.

Slowly as time unfolded, she began to find herself smiling again, and one day, she woke up and her eyes were finally dry. After going through the stages of grief, she was able to begin to slowly take each day one at a time. She slowly started to find beauty in each day and began by finding one or two things daily to be grateful for. She immediately went to work learning everything she could about narcissism, as she was not going to ever do that again! Reading became her favorite past time, and she was crushing a book to a book and a half a week, learning everything and anything she could about life, lessons, healing, re-creating and rebuilding after life throws a curve ball. She found herself buckling down and hibernating to focus on reconnecting with herself, learning to forgive herself and learning to love herself again. She had so much work to do, as this really was an intense period of internal soul searching. She went through the "dark knight of the soul," which felt like an eternal huge black hole of nothingness and sorrow. Anna purposely reminded herself to stay out of the victim zone, but also to appreciate the space she was in and understand that it was okay to feel the emotions. This was all so new for her, as she had never really allowed herself to stop long enough to feel the feelings and address her pain, wants, needs or anything that was shaking her to her core before. It was very uncomfortable.

She found herself reading every evening and watching educational videos and channels to better understand the process she had gone through. She had begun to watch Dr. Ramani's YouTube channel and Andrew Gilroy's NARCDAILY YouTube channel on narcissism to fully understand what had happened in her relationships, learn to identify red flags and patterns, and find tips and tools that would allow her to effectively manage the stages and phases she was going through post-relationship. She learned all about love bombing, gaslighting and the discard phase. As she became more educated about the process, she was able to make sense of what previously did not make sense to her and was finally able to make peace with the realization that it was not all her fault. She still acknowledged her part in the process, and still took responsibility for what she saw as her role in lacking boundaries and remaining silent. It was during these moments that she found peace and comfort in understanding the process that would take place when healing from this type of trauma. She read Dr. Ramini's book, *Should I Stay or Should I Go*, and this also aided her in comprehending what she had gone through. Additionally, she read, *Men Who Hate Women and the Women Who Love Them*, by Dr. Susan Forward and Joan Torres, which helped her get a better understanding of misogynistic behavior. This also was beneficial in helping Anna to understand what she had just come out of and how to prevent this from happening again. This required certain truths about Anna's life experiences and limiting beliefs that needed to be challenged.

During this period of time, Anna deployed the support of those around her to check in, to help her keep her spirits up when she found herself slipping backwards. The need for human interaction and support during this time was very reassuring, and when she did not have the strength, she was able to lean on others to help her get through. She began to really stop and question life, her purpose and what it was all about. During this time, she also examined everything she knew to be true about life. This brought her to a space where she explored spirituality versus religion. She had grown up a devout Catholic her entire life. She never questioned her beliefs, because she knew God exists and Jesus is alive and well. The Holy Spirit is real, and Mother Mary has always been special to her. She grew up in the church, sent her children to Catholic school when they were younger and raised them in the church. She did always wrestle with some of the rules and found some of the manmade rules and interpretations to be a bit contradictory to the God she knew. Some of the philosophies and teachings were challenging for her to accept. She recalled after the second marriage fell apart, she went to see the Priest. She spoke with him about her struggles and sought out his advice. It was during this conversation that he advised that maybe everything she had currently (meaning her and her children) was all she was supposed to have, and he shared some stories about Ruth, and said she did not want to be a woman who had several marriages and that it would be best for her to take some time out of the dating world. Anna was a bit shocked by this response, as she had come for spiritual guidance and felt as if she was looked at as if she was supposed to just accept that this is what life has for her. She refused to accept the picture that he painted and politely thanked him for his time, as she knew that God would not have advised in such a manner.

During this time of growth, she was able to address the questions she had about religion in ways she had not before. She was able to expand her willingness to remain open to exploring the spiritual realm outside of all that had been fed to her from early on in life. It also was during this time that she really deepened and strengthened her relationship with God. Anna went from praying before bed to having way more conversations with God on a daily basis. She also realized that God's divine love for her far exceeded any form of love any human could give to her. This is the love she was seeking and so she began to feel a sense of peace. She focused energies on reading Joyce Meyer's, *Healing the Soul of a Woman*, and then proceeded to read, *The Acts of the Apostles*, and *The Books of Enoch*. All of these readings led her on a quest to seek more and more knowledge and gain a deeper understanding of God's plan and his purpose for her.

From there, Anna began to slowly dig herself out of a hole and joined a women's support group to begin rebuilding her strength. She also began journaling, working with picture journals and continued reading. She pushed through the pain and frustration by working out to keep her body moving. She worked with an energy healer to continue to keep moving and shifting the energy to ensure she was moving stagnant energy and also identifying blockages and chakra imbalances. Anna worked closely with the wellness team to provide support to her physical form, as she continued to go through this very intense AWAKENING. They provided a series of modalities that ranged from supplementation, grounding techniques, breathing techniques, providing a safe space to speak her truth, energy sessions and vibrational tuning sessions. Anna began to learn about the healing power of crystals and so much more.

She shares all of this to say that, often times, we hear people say that you should take time to heal, and if you are anything like Anna, you leave that conversation asking what does that even mean? She had heard that from many people, but when you grow up being taught to just smile, pull up your big girl pants, suck it up, keep moving. You have no idea what healing is, what it means, what is its purpose and how do you do that. It is interesting because internal scars and wounds are not visible to the medical profession, so when the body has finally had enough and revolts, and there is no medical explanation for what is happening, you are at a loss. The best book to describe this process is, *The Body Keeps the Score*, by Bessel van der Kolk.

Healing is a very personal journey. It is one that must be walked alone. There can be others along the way to cheer you on, provide guidance and be available for assistance, but in the end, it is YOU that has to do the work. That work will be different for everyone, but through some trial and error, educating yourself and trying what feels good to your soul, you can heal. Healing does not mean everything that has happened to you goes away. It means that you no longer hide from, stuff the feelings deep down or block out the pain. You deal with it head on, address the areas that feel raw, and you walk through those areas and forgive yourself, bless and release what is holding you back and move through it. The work can be challenging at times, but no one is going to do it for you, and you deserve to live your best life while here on Earth, so having the courage to confront your darkness will always yield great rewards. Going through this process will allow you to restore your hope, belief and find an inner peace that no one can interrupt or take from you.

The reward at the end of this process is a stronger, wiser and healthier version of YOU. A confident, strong individual who has reclaimed YOUR GOD-GIVEN POWER!

SUBCONSCIOUS VERSUS CONSCIOUS

Understanding and recognizing the difference between the subconscious and the conscious, and how they work, is critical. Many of us live in our conscious state our whole lives and did not even realize that exploring and bridging the gap between the subconscious and conscious is possible. Often times, we maneuver through life living on auto pilot and falling into the daily routines that have become our standard process. Rushing and going through life at such a fast pace that we do not even take the time to stop and smell the roses. How often do you sit and ask yourself why you do things the way you do? It is just easier to go with the grain of life, than go against the grain and question societal norms, political views, religious views and the list goes on.

When we operate from the conscious, we are simply operating from a program. A program that has been ingrained throughout all of life's experiences, to include learned limiting beliefs. What is interesting is that is not who we actually are at all. It is not until you uncover and begin to explore your subconscious that you will begin to REMEMBER and realize who you truly are at your core. Only then will you begin to discover your true purpose and understand yourself at the soul level.

Many spend a lifetime trying to figure out how to connect with their subconscious. Many see psychics, hypnotists, undergo therapy and explore many other ways to get in touch with this part of themselves. The subconscious is often referred to as the "higher self." The higher self is your spiritual self, the version of you that is not the most obvious day-to-day operator of your human form. The subconscious operates in the background and keeps the records and history of WHO YOU TRULY ARE AT YOUR CORE. This is the place where intuition and that "gut feeling" comes from when you encounter situations or individuals that make you feel a certain way, whether it being overjoyed, uneasy or as if something is not quite right.

Often during the human experience many get lost or go astray from what their intended purpose was, while here on Earth. It is not uncommon for a human to operate from their lower self, referred to as the conscious self. This can lend itself to operating from the ego-self. This happens often with a less evolved soul. When operating from the low vibrational ego-self, patterns and traits of control, jealousy, anger and superficial behavior are exhibited.

Humans that are more evolved are able to operate from their higher self and see beyond the physical, material and very humanistic traits and behaviors. These evolved beings are able to see life with an entirely different perspective and operate from thoughts from a higher dimension. They often find the human experience to be one that is very basic and limiting. The goal is to bridge the gap between the subconscious and conscious self, so that the human experience can be maximized and experienced through a less limiting perspective. When the higher self and the lower self are in sync TRANSFORMATION, HEALING and AWAKENING truly begin! This is the space where one can truly live, breathe and walk through life as their TRUE AUTHENTIC SELF.

There are so many ways to create synergy to open the doors to the subconscious. As Anna continued on her journey, she found many techniques and opportunities to do the work to discover the beauty of uniting the two. The information she shares is from her journey and her personal experiences. Of course, each person is unique and what worked for her may not be what works for another, but sharing information about her journey is the intention. As Anna continued on her healing path, she remained open and became thirsty for knowledge and experiences that were rooted in the evolution of all aspects of herself. There were specific moments and pivotal points throughout her journey that served purposes for the time and place she was operating from. Below are a few of the most impactful and beneficial experiences that worked for her.

Meditation – She had never experienced or been introduced to formal meditation before this point in her life. She began with some guided meditations that she found on YouTube from Dr. Joe Dispenza. Because she had a really hard time sitting still with herself, she found it easier to listen to guided medications. During this time, she recalls a very specific meditation she completed one evening before bed when she found herself in a very difficult space where her sleep was filled with re-runs of the life that had just disappeared before her eyes. During this meditation, she was focusing on her breath work and literally found herself connecting with another being that was walking towards her, and it had an outline around its body that was an electric blue color. She remembers seeing the hand of that being touching her hand and instantly felt this overwhelming response of, "that is my person" wash over her body. It was after that mediation she realized what had truly happened. She had her first transcendental experience and that was her lower self, connecting with her higher self. The feeling of what happened that evening was truly indescribable and powerful beyond words. From that point forward, she made mediation a priority as she knew it was necessary for her to continue the work to remain in this space of connection.

Journaling – She began journaling through both writing and drawing. As she continued to write, she was able to process moments, emotions and experiences in a way that was more digestible. She also expanded her journaling to drawing after discovering that this method also helps to open the door to the subconscious. She would literally stare at a blank page and just draw whatever came to mind. The shift in her vibration and the positive things happening in her life were almost instant after implementing this approach.

Scans – She faithfully went for her scans and appointments at the wellness center every six to eight weeks to assess her physical health progress. With each session she was able to begin to repair and restore her damaged body. Throughout the course of the scans and follow-up appointments, they were able to narrow down the areas requiring immediate attention and continue to build upon each session. Because Anna's body had gone through so much, the process took some time, and she quickly embraced the concept of trusting the process and those whom she had entrusted her care to as she pushed through. There were moments of great progress as well as frustrations and setbacks, but that was part of the process and as she learned. The wellness center practitioners began by tackling the most critical functions first and that started the journey of restoring her central nervous system. Then, on to detox her organs from the various toxins and poisons. This was the longest part of the journey. After that, it was time to tackle other areas to improve and maximize her physical strength and health. Throughout her treatments she participated in a variety of protocols designed to restore the cells back to healthy functional levels. There were mitochondria resets, supplementation, tinctures, grounding techniques, energy sessions and more that were incorporated to support the process.

Energy Sessions – Game Changer! Anna began one-on-one energy sessions to get started. A combination of methodologies was used during the sessions. At the time, she had no idea what was going on, but the healing benefits were incredible. Vibrational tuning forks, crystals, oils, sound bowls and breathing techniques were all used during the sessions. Focusing on energy flow, meridian points, chakras and energetic blockages were the central focus during the sessions. Restoring energy flow, increasing vibrations and improving overall functionality and balance of the body was the desired outcome of each session.

Group Sound Healing – Anna attended her first group sound healing session and had no idea what she was in for, and it was an indescribable experience. Her first session, she walked in the room and selected a spot on the mat with the cushions. She had several options, mat, chair or the table. She selected the mat on the floor, as she was not sure what to expect for the first experience. As she lay there with a warm covering over her eyes and across her mid-section, she began to hear the slow sound of the sound bowls begin. Next, she heard the sound of the didgeridoo and the gongs. Shortly after, were the sounds of the seashells and, before she knew it, there was an entire symphony playing. It was truly magical. As the sounds surrounded Anna, in what can only be described as a sound bath, she felt her body and mind relax and the meditative state began. It truly was therapeutic. It was as if she was taking a journey through worlds, she knew existed, but had not seen before. As the music played, Anna felt a sense of calm wash over her and she felt at peace. She continued to go to the group sessions several times as she began to see an energetic balance and harmony emerging from the sessions.

By the fourth session something felt very different...very dark. As Anna continued to go further and further into a meditative state, she began to see very dark figures coming towards her and felt her body begin to tense. She was not prepared for what was happening...this was the moment...moment of facing the darkness...her fears! Anna could either go towards the darkness and walk through it, or she could let fear overcome her. It was at this moment that she had to make a split-second decision as to how she was going to face what was coming at her. Anna had come this far, and she knew she could not give up now. As she felt her body begin to shake, and the tears well up, she took a deep breath, and decided not today...not tomorrow...she was not going to be defeated by fear. She was tired of living in pain and fear, and she was determined to walk straight through the darkness and proclaim that SHE IS A CHILD OF GOD, and she had no interest in anything that did not serve the God-given purpose that her soul was here to perform. As she walked towards the darkness and walked through it, she began to feel her body relax, tears flowed and she felt the presence of her Protector, her older brother, who had passed just a few short years prior, and he held her hand as she walked through the darkness and came out the other side.

After that very intense session the following sessions were very calm and relaxing. As she continued to attend the group sessions, she felt continued peace and calm wash over her each time she went. She felt her chakras coming back to life and her energy began flowing so much freer. The blockages and the challenges she had faced before in her human form, became so fluid and functional. The group sound healing classes allowed her to begin to operate and push her own energy through her body and continue with the healing process.

LIVING ON AUTOPILOT

Anna had always been able to operate at a level far exceeding the average ability to multi-task. She recalled once being asked if she did drugs, because the observer mentioned that he had never seen someone operate at such a high rate of speed with such precision. Anna was very perplexed by this response from him. She had been operating at optimal efficiency her whole life and thought that was normal. At work, everyone joked and called her the hard drive, who always remembered everything, and she was known for multi-tasking within an inch of her life. One day she woke up and realized she was not able to function and multi-task at a level that was beyond normal. It was not until her whole world fell apart, and she could barely function, that she found herself sitting in the waiting room of the wellness clinic before realizing there was another way. Her former self had a very predictable routine. Anna would wake up at a certain time, make her lemon water, celery juice and began her day chasing after kids, working a high-profile job and handling household business.

Little did she know that there was an actual name and term for what she was doing. It is called LIVING ON AUTOPILOT. The first time she had heard this phase she remembered thinking...ah yes...that is exactly how she lives her life. It came up during a session with her energy healer and she looked at him dumbfounded. As soon as he said it, she felt it in her core and realized that that is exactly what she had done her whole life. She had learned that if she operated at the speed of light and moved faster than her mind, she could escape all of the hurt, pain and darkness that had and was occurring. She could simply convince herself that all was well, and everything was fine...she was fine...life was great. The truth was, if she had stopped long enough to process everything that had happened and was happening, she would probably have lost her s***!

For many, living on autopilot becomes a way to survive when living a life that is solely focused on being in survival mode. The body is not designed to live in survival mode for extended periods of time. Following a structured routine allows the body and mind to get used to a very familiar routine that does not require one to think too deeply about what is happening. It is somewhat of a coping mechanism for self-preservation.

SHADOW WORK

Shadow work is part of the formula Anna used on her journey...for Anna it was an essential ingredient in the recipe to healing and reconnecting to the soul! Healing requires exploring parts of the conscious and unconscious mind to identify and uncover repressed events, traumas and experiences that you have intentionally or unintentionally hidden from your conscious self. This is where the inner work comes in, "sitting with yourself" and trying approaches and techniques to figure out what works best for you.

Interestingly enough, Anna had been familiar with the terminology of being the light, finding the light, walking towards the light, but she had not really explored the aspect of her own darkness, which at some level, exists in all of us. She was not familiar with the term "dark night of the soul" up until this point, but it arrived right on time after the realization of all of the traumatic events in her life began to surface and the avalanche of emotions unleashed. It was during this period of time that she knew she had to act, and act swiftly, to ensure she was moving forward and not staying in a place of sadness for too long, or in a zone where she would get stuck in the overwhelm of emotion. The goal was to feel the emotion, experience it, accept it and release it.

This was the time period in her life that she had to learn to use her mental fortitude to literally fight for herself and reconnect with her higher self! This was the beginning of the process of experiencing the evolution of her soul. She began exploring information about the process of going through this dark painful time. She also started applying different techniques to work in this space. When you hear "dark night," it is no joke...there were moments when she had to literally pull herself up and say, "you can do this," and just keep pushing. She knew that there would be a light at the end of the tunnel, and she repeatedly used her favorite mantra "this is only temporary," to keep reminding herself that she could get through this time and space.

Shadow work is not always easy, but it was worth every second of the process. It helped Anna to learn who she truly is at her core. It was an opportunity to see what she was truly made of when she was stripped of everyone and everything that she thought she was in her life. It was a moment in time where she got to REMEMBER who she was at her soul level and re-create her reality and work towards what she desired versus continuing through life blindly.

Some examples of shadow work that she implemented during her journey include:

- ***Sitting with Herself*** *– Just being still and allowing herself to go through the emotions and process what had happened in her life up until now.*

- ***Journaling*** *- Expressing her feelings and capturing her emotions through journaling assisted in Anna getting in touch with what was going on internally with her. This also allowed for some reflection, forgiveness and closure to take place as she wrote her way through many difficult conversations and thoughts. Additionally, this was an opportunity for her to create and re-create her desires going forward.*

- ***Meditation*** *– Guided, as well as self-guided, meditations with emphasis and focus on breath work. Inner child meditations allowed her to reconnect with her child-like self and make peace with many unhealed wounds that she carried with her throughout her lifetime. This allowed her to quiet her mind, just be and connect with her higher self.*

- ***Dream Analysis*** *– As ruminating thoughts and memories appeared, she would journal through the nightmares and pain. This also was an opportunity and space for her to create visions for her future.*

- ***Energy Work*** *– Participating in individual energy sessions to adjust and support her vibrations and frequency to counteract the negative emotions processing through her body. This provided her with a safe space to work through darkness and traumas in a way* *that did not require her to sit on a therapist's couch and verbally express her thoughts and feelings. Also, she was able to use the guidance of blockages and trapped energy to figure out what chakras were out of alignment and required attention to restore balance.*

- **Grounding Techniques** – *Learning and practicing grounding techniques was essential for Anna. When she would begin to feel off balance or not quite present in the moment, she was able to use various techniques to anchor herself.*

- **Affirmations** – *Identifying "I AMs" throughout this phase of her healing was crucial. This practice assisted her in being invested in pushing forward, remaining positive and focusing on the way forward and her progress.*

- **Physical Exercise** – *This was a huge thing for Anna. She always worked through her stress or whatever was troubling her by exerting physical energy through the form of exercise. She always had a passion for working out and the feeling and sense of accomplishment that results from a good hard workout. For this reason, she found that kickboxing was her jam. In the past, Zumba was her go to, as she found that music had the power to immediately shift her energy levels. She returned to Zumba and immediately felt the shift change when she was in class. Additionally, incorporating a regular routine of physical exercise was beneficial at keeping the energy flow through the muscles going and assisted with losing up areas of stress and tension that she previously would experience tension.*

There are so many different approaches and forms of shadow work and, because everyone's needs vary, it is important to try different methodologies until you find what resonates with you. Anna found this time period to be the most stressful, challenging and debilitating. It was as if a train had run her over and then backed up and went over her again and again. There were good days and bad days and then, eventually, over time she started to experience better than bad. She would find herself moving forward and then a dream would pop up or a memory and it would send her spiraling. She would listen to several YouTube channels that were very informative about what she was going through, and this helped her to understand the different phases that many go through when in this part of the healing process. Some of her favorite public figures who served as inspirations for Anna were Dr. Joe Dispenza, Tony Robbins, Anthony William, Oprah Winfrey, Esther Hicks, Jerry Hicks, Donna Eden, Lisa Bilyeu and Dr. Ramani Durvasula.

All of these experts and their resources (i.e., books, podcasts, YouTube channels, live events, etc.) provided very insightful information that helped her to understand what was happening and assisted her in validating what she experienced and the associated feelings and responses. When trauma and abuse are experienced, it can be difficult to depict what is and is not real and what feelings are and are not valid. One can begin to doubt yourself and lose a sense of reality. It can begin to get confusing when trying to figure out what is fact and fiction. It was during this time Anna had to find the courage and strength to keep going. Fortunately, she had a very high tolerance for pain and will power that does not quit so she decided that she would call on God for the good and bad moments. When she did not know if she could handle the pain or if she felt her strength slowly withering, she knew GOD would be strong for her and help carry her through.

This phase was filled with a lot of darkness...a very cold sense of emptiness. A feeling of loneliness and loss of what could have been, should have been and the realization that the sunshine and rainbows she had been focusing on her whole life was just a figment of her imagination. Her world and the view she had chosen to look through was a farce. It was a made-up conglomeration of experiences that she created to cope with what was really happening. This was the hardest part. Realizing that throughout her entire life she had been used, played like a pawn in the game of chess, just moved around on the board with no voice to express how she truly felt. She had simply become a puppet with many puppet masters throughout the years. Going from one to the next and continuing to re-create patterns and cycles that did not serve her or her soul's purpose. A girl whose life had been interrupted and a soul that was lost.

EVOLUTION OF THE SOUL

As we go through life it is essential for growth and evolution to continuously occur. Not only is our human form evolving, but our soul is as well. Most people go through life asleep, not awakened or acknowledging their personal truth. Many roam this Earth in human form unaware of who they are, what they are here for and spend a lifetime following the masses. This results in missing out on the purpose of why they are here and completely oblivious to the journey of their individual unique soul.

The soul occupies the body and yet is still a mystery to many. We know it exists, as several studies have been conducted throughout the times to prove that a body is lighter after the body experiences death. Many have concluded that this is because once the body experiences death the soul departs the body decreasing its weight. There also have been many witness accounts of physically observing the soul departing the body after a loved one has died.

As we go through life, we are faced with the struggles of living the human life and trying to understand a spiritual space that we cannot always physically observe. This is where the introduction of Faith is awakened. Having Faith that there is something bigger and greater than ourselves. For this reason, it is necessary to acknowledge and respect the soul that is housed in the human body. Caring for, respecting and connecting with the soul is imperative and allows space for the conscious and subconscious to work collaboratively. As the soul evolves, lessons are learned and new levels of life experiences are unlocked, much like a video game.

HUMAN-TO-HUMAN RELATIONSHIPS

Human relationships are some of the most complicated, complex, multi-faceted experiences a human can encounter. They are filled with highs and lows where emotions, limiting beliefs, an individual's past traumas as well as generational trauma can either be subdued or exacerbated. All too often when relationships begin, they start off in the honeymoon phase and then, fast forward a few years later and those same precious moments can either result in a lifetime bond of friendship, love, happiness and partnership, or turn into a place for pain to grow and expose all of the unresolved wounds in a person's mind, body and spirit.

Who we choose to enter into relationships with can truly impact our lives far beyond what we may initially imagine. Those whom we choose to surround ourselves with will have an impact on our daily experiences in our physical space, our home, work and finances. A person's inner circle, typically the closest, will determine the quality of experience a person will have during their life experiences. For this reason, it is incredibly important to be very selective and careful about who is allowed into our personal energy space.

Romantic relationships are often a tangled web filled with passion and pain. These are some of the most personal and intimate relationships that can make or break a person's human experience. Being selective and careful when allowing others to enter into this space or accepting their energy into your energetic space is necessary for each one of us to evaluate.

When a relationship is healthy, it can elevate the human experience and serve as a space for personal growth and emulates a sense of freedom. When a relationship is toxic, it can create an environment of suffocation and negative energy, hindering the individual from personal and spiritual growth. For this reason, it is necessary to meet individuals where they are, and ideally each person should be whole before entering the relationship. If either of the individuals in the relationship are not whole, it will create an environment and opportunity for issues of co-dependence to surface. If the two in the relationship are not equally yoked, the relationship may begin well, but over time, will result in many challenges and frustrations and often times result in feelings of unfulfillment. This can also lend itself to a level of toxicity transpiring that could have disastrous consequences for individuals involved in the relationship and also to current and future generations of those involved.

RE-CREATION

An interesting choice of words. What does it mean to re-create something? Re-creation can best be described as taking something from the past or something that existed in the past and re-living or remaking that same experience or very similar. Essentially, you are creating that "something" that has been experienced before and creating it again.

The purpose for deciding to re-create something is one that should be examined on a subconscious level, when choosing to implement in the human experience. Often times, re-creation continues to keep us caught up in generational trauma, as well as cycles and patterns of unhealthy behavior. In essence, it keeps us stuck doing and being what we have been taught and were shown. It stifles the opportunity to break the mold and allow for creativity. Re-creation is simply a re-enactment of what has already taken place previously. Such as repetitive patterns, behaviors, lifestyles, etc. For example, if someone came from a family of business owners, it would be expected that the individual also would become a business owner, because that is the family history. If someone came from a family that had generations and generations of trauma, whether it be physical, emotional, mental, alcohol, gambling, etc., it would become the pattern of behavior that repeats itself without question, because that is how it has always been.

Re-creation is simply re-enforcement and acceptance of what has always been and continuing to carry forth that behavior, tradition or pattern. Often times, this is done mindlessly, as it becomes so engrained in the human mind and body, that there is no time for thought or questioning because it has always been this way.

Re-creation is what plagues so many human beings, families, generations and those who have not arrived on Earth yet. Because humans are typically creatures of habit. The habits and beliefs that are developed throughout the experiences of early childhood and through teens years are very deeply engrained in your mind. It is from these perspectives that morals and values typically form. Exposure to life, relationships, religion, work ethic and so much more is often the basis for ideals that are developed about the human experience. The human experience and expectations are often dependent on the quality of experience and exposure to life events.

Anna's story was one that clearly demonstrated re-creation. What is interesting is that Anna did not even realize she was re-creating the life and similar patterns of all of the women who had come before her in her ancestry. She recalled, when she was getting married the first time, her mother saying, "why do you want my life?" At the time, she had no clue what her mother was talking about. Her mother would often make comments and remarks about how hard Anna was making her life and, truthfully, Anna did not know how to do it any other way. This was a learned trait and behavior she had adopted over time. She had seen her mother always so strong and just getting things done. Anna just assumed that being strong was how to get things done. When things went haywire, she just knew she needed to pull up her big girl pants and keep it moving.

After leaving her second marriage, Anna decided it was time to take a long hard look at her life and what had transpired thus far to keep seeing similar patterns and trends occur in her romantic relationships. When she was able to analyze her relationship patterns and behaviors, she noticed some similarities between the type of men that entered her life. She saw commonalities between the personalities and spirits of the men. They had very charismatic personalities, maintained a positive public image, were very funny, likeable and smooth talkers. They all possessed a very confident outward appearance. So, the question she had to ask and dig deep to find the answer to, was...why was she attracting these manipulative men who were rooted in ego and had an ultimate goal of exerting power over love? The answers were not as easily identifiable as she expected them to be...the answers came through a lot of soul searching, digging deep and addressing traumas she did not even know she had experienced.

The search for answers led her to the very beginning of her human experience. She had to walk back through her childhood years. It was during this quest for answers that she realized the deep dark secrets that had been buried for years. She discovered the early childhood traumas and the repetitive cycle of domineering, power and money hungry men that surrounded her upbringing. It was through this exposure that she became familiar with this type of personality. It was where she developed most of her limiting beliefs about her role as a female and the need to seek male approval for validation of who and what she was. Looking back at it, she realized how backwards this was and how incredibly foolish she had been to give her power away to such unworthy men. At the time, it seemed the appropriate thing to do...be a great girlfriend...be an exceptional wife...be a great mother and do not rock the boat. The fear of these men leaving her was an unshakeable fear she had always held deep down. She did not want to lose whatever little affection they would provide for her. She did not want to be alone...she wanted a family. Reality was...that desire for a family had, ultimately, cost her -- her power, her happiness, her dignity, her self-esteem, her health and, ultimately, almost cost her - her life.

As Anna began to share her story more openly amongst those assisting her on her healing journey, and with her close family members, she began to uncover some very surprising information. She had not really ever looked into her family heritage and did not know much beyond her immediate grandparents. She was aware of where both sides of her family originated from, but never knew their stories or their dynamics. As she continued to learn and look back through generations of women and men in her family, she was shocked to discover that she too had re-created very similar romantic relationships. Anna learned about the cycles of abuse that the women in her family endured. The central theme of power-hungry men, who were domineering and did not value their women, was astonishing. Initially, she tried to make sense of it by rationalizing the time period and the relationship dynamics for that era, but the stories continued to have shocking similarities. With each story told, Anna became sadder and sadder, realizing that she too had carried the same torch into her relationships. This was the point where she stood up and said NO MORE. It had to end somewhere, and for this reason, she vowed not to allow her life to continue in this manner and decided her voice would not go unheard. She had decided to officially **BREAK THE CYCLE OF RE-CREATION** and change the direction of women in her family's lives for generations to come!

CREATION

The opposite of re-creation is CREATION! An opportunity to live out the human experience freely without a framework or being placed in a box and being told how to live, when to live, where to live or with a sea of preconceived notions and expectations. In other words, living without limitations or societal pressures and demands. No molding, no conformity and no expectations being impressed upon the human experience. Just free will, freedom of choice and freedom of expression. After all, is that not why your soul arrived on Earth...to create?

The essence of life is "CREATION." The human experience is designed for creation. It is up to each and every one who chooses to participate in the human experience to create the life to be experienced by that individual. This is why we have the term "in- dividual," and we also have the term "oneness." We are all individuals having a human experience that is rooted in the collective conscious experience also known as "oneness". All too often, many walk around sleeping just going through the motions, living on autopilot and succumbing to the environments in which they are born and live. As a result, many attract and give off vibrations that attract the exact opposite of what they are desiring and wishing to experience causing them to encounter and experience everything they did not want to experience. This is what Anna came to learn about her human experience, once she began to go through her own personal awakening. Through studying and learning the cause and effects of the laws of attraction, she could start to identify some of the rationale behind some of the unintended experiences that attracted into her energetic field. Once you are awakened...you learn just how differently your life can be!

Each and every day is an opportunity to create the experiences you desire ultimately shaping the human experience. Whether that be to live out a dream, travel, create a family, experience relationships, a career or just existing, each person has an opportunity to live out their desires. Each and every human being has the ability to tap into their creative side to choose what human experience is to be had. The part that is challenging is removing the layers of taught behaviors, feelings, emotions and all that has been programmed into your subconscious. In order to dream you have to get out of the box that life has placed you in...awaken your soul...merge your conscious and subconscious and begin to dream again!

WHERE DO I START?

As Anna pondered all of this new information available, which was totally different than anything she had ever been used to hearing, learning or experiencing...she felt lost. Feelings of overwhelm and confusion rushed through her thoughts and mind as she felt like the world, as she knew it, was disappearing slowly. The matrix had become her new reality! Everything she thought she knew, and her way of life all these years, seemed too full of contradictions, confusion and an emptiness of her purpose. She quickly realized that this moment in time was an opportunity for her to embrace a new way of thinking, being and living. She put on her seat belt and decided to buckle up for the ride. No more fear...no more doubt...just a quest for health, healing, truth and authenticity.

SURRENDER

As humans, we feel a need to control our thoughts, experiences, emotions and all that occurs around us. It is a natural instinct to want to have some sense of organization, expectation, outcome and control over our daily lives, our future hopes and dreams. For goodness sakes, this is what is pretty much taught throughout our lives. You are born, follow your parents' rules, go to school...follow more rules, grow up, get a job and adhere to all of those rules too. Somewhere in the already well constructed rules and guidelines of how to behave, act and live, you look for any semblance of your life to have some control over. Often times, we spend countless hours setting goals, creating vision boards and creating safety mechanisms to ensure we have total control over the outcomes of our goals and predictions. Without control, we feel out of balance, unable to figure out how to function and often many feel lost. What does all of this "need for control" do to the human body? It creates the opposite effect of what is desired. Instead, the body goes into a constant state of stress response. A loop that begins a cycle that if not broken will wreak havoc on the human body over time. There is only one way to break free from this stress response...***SURRENDER.***

Surrender does not necessarily come easy, but it is the only way to break free from the human response to control everything and anything that comes across your life's path. Surrendering requires a great deal of FAITH, HOPE, TRUST and BELIEVING. BELIEVING that God is walking with YOU, lives within YOU and is holding your hand every step of the way. Read that again... BELIEVING. BELIEVING that God is walking with YOU!

Surrendering requires a great deal of energy and effort if you have been fighting against the grain your whole life. This is the part where you learn to exercise self-love, gratitude, Faith, compassion and belief. You have to let go of everything you know and all that you think is necessary, to do, day after day and begin to trust. To listen to your intuition...to have conversations with God. You have to truly believe and stop second guessing what is happening in and around you. Once you surrender and give it over to God, all things begin to work in your favor. You are now working with the flow of energetic vibrations, the universe and all things that are meant for you.

BE STILL, QUIET YOUR MIND AND SIT WITH YOURSELF

What does that mean? Everyone always talks about being still and quieting your mind and for all the Type A personalities out there, the concept of "being still" seems like torture. Being still is one of the hardest things for a person, especially for those on the go all the time, and can be a difficult obstacle to overcome. It is a skill and does not necessarily come naturally to many people.

Anna recalls sitting in Linda's office and hearing her say that all will change and begin to work in her favor when she learns to "sit with it." She looked at Linda and said, "What does that even mean?" Linda just looked at her and smiled and said, "When you learn to appreciate the space you are in." Baffled and confused, Anna walked out that day thinking that could not be too hard. Just kidding...it was very hard. Sitting still, looking around and seeing that the life she thought she had created was no longer, there was this constant pain in her heart that left her feeling unsettled and, on some level, like a failure for not being able to "make it work." It was crippling, and some days a paralyzing feeling and the thoughts were more than she could bear. There were a lot of tears, written and burnt letters, hard workouts to push out the frustration, anger and a feeling of loneliness and isolation.

It was not until Anna began to feel more settled with the new direction of her life that she began to appreciate and accept the value that "sitting with it" brought to her life. Each day seemed to get easier and easier. She began to surrender to the idea that the version of life she thought she had was not meant for her. Her purpose was bigger than what that life could offer. She was not in alignment with God's purpose, and when she began to realize this, she started to feel a shift. Slowly, each day got easier and easier. She began to get excited about a future that did not have a concrete path. All of a sudden, she was free to create...create beyond her wildest dreams. No more hiding, no more living someone else's dream, no more running someone else's business, no more being disrespected, being invalidated and being fed breadcrumbs. SHE WAS FREE! FREE to sit with herself and process all that had happened in her life. No more giving her power away. No more giving her energy and effort to people who were only meant to be a steppingstone in her life... those who were sent to be a wake-up call to awaken her to her true life's purpose.

It was during this time that Anna began to practice self-care for the first time in a long time. She found herself exploring things she enjoyed. She would meditate, take walks, go to work out classes and spend time enjoying the beautiful children that God had blessed her with. For the first time, she was able to interact and spend time with her children without someone interfering or making her feel like she was a worthless mother. The feeling was freeing. They were all able to sit calmly and peacefully in their home and process all of the traumas and darkness that had loomed over them for far too long. It was the most peaceful and healing space they all had ever been in together.

Being still and quieting your mind may appear to be terrifying in the beginning. But once you learn the skill, it can be one of the most freeing experiences you can have. You will quickly realize that it is all part of the process!

TRAUMA'S EFFECT ON THE BODY

Trauma's effect on the body is profound. With many new illnesses affecting the human population day-by-day, it is absolutely astonishing that there are not alarms calling all of us out to explore what is going on. Nowadays, there is a prescription, therapy or a magical potion for every symptom imaginable. The sad part is...this is just a band-aid placed over the real problem. How does trauma affect the body and its ability to function?

The truth is...trauma manifests in the body as illness more often than diagnosed. This was best explained in the book, *The Body Keeps the Score*, by Bessel A. Van der Kolk. In this book, he explores so much about trauma that gets trapped in the body and its effect on human experience and behaviors. Another great resource was, *When the Body Says No*, by Gabor Mate, which, the author describes the connection between stress and disease and walks the reader through ways to address and heal from this effect.

Throughout Anna's experience, one of the things that the doctor's never looked at was the possibility of any of her symptoms stemming from trauma. Anna had not thought of this either, as the medical professionals she entrusted with her care were sure it was autoimmune related or possibly a genetic issue. When Anna persisted to advocate for herself, they continued to look at her as if she had lost her mind. They felt that they had done all they could and ran every test and that was the end of that. The therapists had written her off as being perfectly within normal anxiety and stress limits for the number of physical ailments she was exhibiting.

It was not until Anna had entered the space of energy work that the root causes for her body's experiences were uncovered. It was during this part of the process that the TRUTH was uncovered. It was through the combination of changing her mindset, educating herself about the life experiences she had been through, trauma healing, proper nutrition and supplementation, energy work, sound healing, energy sessions, grounding and meditation techniques that she began to experience relief.

Slowly, but surely with each trauma she uncovered, she was able to shed layers and layers and wall after wall of buried traumas. She was able to see that her most recent situation had opened up old wounds and scars. It seemed to add additional scars and traumas on top of her already burdened physical body. As the new traumas piled on, so did the weight. The physical weight was a symptom...another physical message being sent from above that she was on the wrong path. A path that did not serve her, her children or her purpose. Changing physical form was the last attempt from above to send the signal to Anna that it was time to wake up!

As Anna slowly awakened, she was overcome with emotion with what she uncovered. She felt lost, lonely and completely defeated. She quickly surrounded herself with a team of the most powerful energetic beings she had encountered. She knew they were all sent to be part of her healing journey. She knew the only way to work through it all was to walk through it. Grounding became a huge technique she had to use to help her calm her body down and center herself. She would immerse herself in nature and walk bare foot and plant her feet in the soil looking up to the sky. This process allowed her to re-connect with Mother Earth.

FOOD AND NUTRITION MATTER

It was during this stage where Anna learned all about the Medical Medium protocols that she became educated about the importance of nutrition and how food can serve as a source of healing to the body. Anna began to learn the power of proper nutrition and its ability to assist with healing and restoring functions of the   body. For example, she learned that spirulina, cilantro, ginger, turmeric, Atlantic dulse flakes, wild blueberries, honey, bananas and oranges can make an amazing detox smoothie that can assist the body in clearing out heavy metals naturally. She also learned that freshly juiced and strained celery can aid in removing toxins from the body. Papaya also can be used to help soothe and aid in supporting the functions of the liver.

Also, the power of greens is tremendous at ensuring the body has the vitamins and minerals it needs to operate in the highly polluted environments we live in today. Anna discovered the power of many herbs and minerals found throughout the organic markets. She found herself making fresh turmeric and ginger shots regularly. The reality is, with the on-the-go lifestyles and health issues that continue to plague our society, it is unbelievable that we do not realize that we could all benefit from a lesson in proper nutrition. The food today is not the food from a few decades ago. Many changes to the foods available in our grocery stores today make it necessary to become educated on what we are actually consuming.

When Anna began to follow the Medical Medium protocols, she learned just how important it was to pay attention to labels and buy organic, whenever possible. Because she began eating so many fresh fruits and vegetables and began juicing many of them, it was necessary to observe, monitor and minimize how much exposure to pesticides, preservatives and additives were in many of the foods she consumed. Also, eating raw fruits and vegetables required paying special attention to the possibility of consuming chemicals that could be counterproductive to what she was trying to accomplish by healing and nourishing her body through a solid healthy nutritional plan. During this time, she also expanded her scope of learning by reading many books by Dr. Sebi and also Dr. Terry Wahls, who wrote *The Wahls Protocol.*

SUPPLEMENTATION CAN ONLY GET YOU SO FAR

Supplementation can be a viable solution to balancing and supporting many functions of the body. They are designed to assist and aid in the body's deficiencies that may be caused by a lack of nutrition or illness. Often times, our diets and daily lifestyles become deficient in certain key nutrients and go unnoticed until the body begins to exhibit symptoms causing concern. Understanding and learning about the various supplements, their purpose and the proper use for each is essential to understanding what is appropriate for your body. Working with a doctor or wellness professional, who is well versed in supplementation and is able to identify any deficiencies in the body, is an essential part of the process ensuring the correct combination and dosages are taken. Conducting your own independent research is necessary to ensuring you are informed as to what you are putting in your body as well as what to expect as an outcome.

Throughout Anna's healing journey, she explored alternative approaches to healing. When the doctors prescribed a medication, she would immediately seek out a more natural or holistic alternative. She first explored supplementation when she began following the Medical Medium protocols. It was during this time that she went through an exhaustive list of supplements to learn their purpose and function. She later was re-introduced to supplementation protocols when working with the chiropractor, who provided a customized protocol specifically for the condition of her health during that time period.

Later, in her healing journey when she was seeing the wellness team, they conducted a variety of assessments to include scanning to identify a treatment plan for her. Anna received a protocol listing that was created to address her unique individual needs. These modalities uncovered several areas in her body that required immediate attention.

The first order of business was to restore her central nervous system. The supplementation protocol prescribed was prescribed to support the key areas that were being addressed. Resetting her cells, mitochondria reset and aiding the body to stop operating in survival mode was critical. The all-natural remedies were just what her body needed.

She began a regiment of supplements, in conjunction with other techniques, such as meditation, grounding and journaling. The combination was essential to aid and support in her body's restoration and healing process. Additionally, this formula provided her with a very concrete way for her to gauge and track her progress. Because Anna was very data and metric focused, this gave her the extra assurance she needed to know that she was making progress. Anna stayed the course...trusted in the process and followed the protocols. Because of her dedication and persistence, she experienced a complete shift and restoration in her nervous system. The whole process took almost a full year but was worth every second of the work she put into it. The sessions and support from Linda and Nathan also were critical to her success. During times when she felt lost and uncertain, they provided the extra encouragement she needed to push through!

From that point forward, their focus was on cleaning up more manageable areas of her body. Because Anna had been poisoned, her body and organs had undergone an attack that had impacted most of her body's functions. Her hormones, thyroid and thymus were all on the list. Linda methodically attacked each of these areas one at a time, until restoration and healing was complete before moving on to the next area to address.

UNWRAPPING SPIRITUAL GIFTS

Each and every one of us has spiritual gifts. If we are fortunate to go through an awakening process in our lifetime, our gifts are revealed in a way that just happens over time. Many may go through life on autopilot or blind to the fact that such blessings exist. It is our responsibility and mission to unwrap and use these gifts in a way that serves the greater good. The key is to be grateful and thankful for these gifts and ensure that they are used in a manner that serves the mission that God has set forth. Misuse and abuse of these gifts will ultimately result in consequences. It is important to remember that "the Lord giveth and the Lord taketh." So, being responsible for the blessings entrusted to us is paramount. Showing gratitude is an ideal practice that should be adopted along the way, if not already in play.

Gratitude is a key ingredient in walking the path to getting closer to seeing your spiritual gifts. In a world full of hustle and bustle, it can be tempting to steer off course and, in some cases, even get lost in the negative of life's misfortunes. Being intentional about practicing gratitude is a practice that will assist all in remaining focused on the beauty and blessings of life. A practice that Anna found to be helpful early on in this area was daily gratitude journaling. This got her into the conscious habit of identifying things to be grateful for, even when she was experiencing hardships. This allowed her to shift her focus and her attention to the good and steer clear of getting in a rut of focusing on what she thought she should have or be experiencing.

As Anna continued along the path to awakening, she began to explore her spiritual gifts. Realizing that each and every one of us has our own unique God-given spiritual gifts, Anna began to have conversations with God to explore her spiritual gifts. Anna soon found guides appearing in her life in physical form. She knew God had begun placing others in her path so that she could begin to awaken to who she truly was and see her purpose.

During a trip back home to visit with her family, she was provided an opportunity to connect with a woman, Angela, who became a spiritual guide on Anna's journey. She recalled the earlier days when beginning the process of unwrapping her own spiritual gifts and, as part of her mission, she had devoted and dedicated time to others who were seeking wisdom and guidance along this very new path. She spent two days walking Anna and her mother through so many different tools and techniques. They did some very in-depth inner child meditations.

She also shared, with Anna and her mother, how to interpret auras. This included understanding the color schemes of the auras. She also provided some lessons geared towards a deeper understanding of the chakras and the role they play in balancing and harmonizing the body. Anna was slightly familiar with aura readings, as she had learned about them a few years prior when a cousin, Gabriela, had begun offering aura sessions. She had performed readings on Anna and her children and Anna found them to be very informative. She examined the reports and was able to receive an aura photograph that visually demonstrated her energy field with relation to chakras. Once the session concluded, she had a better understanding of her aura and how her energy fields worked.

REFLEXOLOGY

Angela also introduced Anna and her mother to the practice of reflexology. During the session, Anna was instructed to lie on the table and get comfortable. She closed her eyes and decided to relax. As she allowed herself to relax, the energy began to flow through her body and Angela began working on the movement of energy throughout her body. As Angela identified areas where trapped energy was present, she would work with Anna's energy to move it through her body. It was during this time that she identified the childhood wounds, where energy had gotten trapped in her solar plexus. She was able to provide Anna with some very practical ways to address this black bubble-like structure that was blocking her chakra. She advised Anna to keep working on the inner child meditations so that she could continue to heal this deep wound that was holding her back.

Additionally, she was able to identify several areas in Anna's foot that had crystal deposits that linked to the area of her thymus. She recommended that Anna utilize a rolling apparatus that was designed for reflexology treatments to address crystal deposits found in the feet.

CRYSTALS

Crystals offer a variety of purposes to include energy channeling and healing. There are so many different crystals, and each has a very specific purpose. Understanding and educating yourself about crystals and usages is very helpful when determining which crystals are best for an individual. Knowing how and when to use them is an important part of the process when introducing them into use.

During Anna's visit with Angela, she shared her knowledge of crystals with both she and her mother. She gave a brief overview of each one and the purposes for each, and they had an opportunity to see them. Anna had been introduced to crystals previously but had not fully explored or understood their purpose or how they were used. Angela provided valuable insights and really expanded the knowledge they had previously learned.

There were so many things to choose from. She quickly became drawn to amethyst and rose quartz. She explored their properties and ways to integrate them into her current spiritual experience and practices. Once she figured out which ones were for her, she learned how to pick crystals based on a process of putting her hands over the crystals to feel the energy coming from them. She made her selections of the size, cut and feel of the stone, based on her energetic response to the ones she selected.

AFFIRMATIONS

The introduction of affirmations into daily practices also is extremely important and assists with focusing energies in a positive direction. Affirmations can be extremely powerful if they are specific and relevant to the person incorporating them. There are so many resources available to support you in getting started with affirmations if this is something new to you.

Anna found herself identifying affirmations that resonated with her soul. She found herself journaling affirmations, drawing pictures and even writing her affirmations in lipstick on her bathroom mirror. For several months she would walk in her bathroom every morning and the first thing she would see would be the dark maroon lipstick affirmations that said, "I AM healing and getting stronger every day," and "I AM calm." She would take a few moments each day to look at the words and really connect with them.

She also recalls reading and incorporating many affirmations from Joyce Meyer's works. As she would stumble across affirmations in her social media feeds that resonated with her, she would screen shot, download or repost ones that she felt connected to. She continued to exercise affirmations daily as part of her spiritual practice and eventually found herself retraining her mind and body to believe again!

THE WEIGHT LOSS MYSTERY...

Then, the final challenge...despite all of the healing taking place, a year with personal trainers and regulated diet, Anna could not shed the mysterious weight that she had accumulated during the last year she was with Lionel. It appeared quickly, without explanation and had not wanted to depart. It was at this stage of the healing process that it was recommended that Anna begin working with Michael to participate in his Primal Reset program.

Anna was up for the opportunity, as she was determined to come back to the world better and stronger than when she walked through the wellness clinic's front door. She signed up for the program and began the four-week long reset. During the reset, there was a specific protocol that called for usage of oils and assessing the rate of absorption in the skin. After several rounds of this protocol, Anna continued to document that her body was not absorbing the oil. Upon conclusion of the four-week program, she was re-evaluated for overall health progress using scans and a steamy reset. During the steamy reset, Michael noticed that it took quite some time for Anna's body to begin sweating despite the high temperatures of the steaming and oil treatments administered. As he appeared a bit perplexed by this, upon further discussion, it was determined that Anna's liver was not working efficiently and there was another lingering effect of a body overburdened by toxins and undoubtedly another side effect of having been poisoned.

Anna was beyond frustrated, because it seemed as if one thing was fixed, it felt like another was becoming a never-ending story, and she was so done with all of it! She battled frustration, anger and complete disbelief that such evil had occurred, but was thankful that God stood by her and ensured she came out alive and able to recover. Regardless of the length of time it was going to take her to heal, she began to appreciate, become more grateful and practice gratitude for the human life that she was given. She knew things could have turned out very differently, so she decided to put the pain and hurt aside and get to work!

Now that the weight loss mystery had been solved, she was given specific directions on what to do next. She needed to force her body to sweat. What did this mean? She was given instructions to induce sweating at least fifteen to twenty minutes daily, preferably in the sauna to get started. By doing this, her body would get used to sweating, push out the toxins being detoxed from her body and create less burden on the liver. By doing this, she would be able to free her body from the trauma it had experienced. Anna decided to take it a step further and get a sauna suit for her workouts, to move the process along quicker as she was very much ready to shed all of the weight of her past and be free from all of the resonance of anything associated with it! It was during this sweating process that she began to see the weight drop and she continued to see results as she continued to restore the health and function of her liver and increase the functionality of her body's lymphatic system.

ENERGY & VIBRATIONS

Everything begins and ends with energy. Anna had heard this theory before, but never really knew what that meant or put too much thought into it. When she thought of energy, she would think of electricity in the sense that it sends and conducts electricity to allow for light. What she learned on her journey shocked her and opened her eyes to a whole new way of looking at life.

We are energy. We conduct...give and receive energy all day long. As long as you have a pulse, you are sending and receiving energy to everything you encounter. Who knew this whole time, as she was struggling with health issues, the secret was in moving her own energy and not allowing it to get stuck. Anna also learned that there is a giving and receiving side of the body. She did not know that hugging had such a strong energetic effect and furthermore, the way someone gives and receives a hug is even more important. For example, hugging with the right arm gives energy and hugging with the left receives energy for the one initiating the hug. Anna was such a hugger when she met people, which meant that, depending on who she was interacting with meant that she could be giving and/or receiving energy that she may or may not have wanted to intentionally experience.

Then, there was the whole educational process of learning more in-depth about feminine and masculine energy. Anna knew that every human being has the ability to operate in feminine or masculine energy spaces independent of their gender. Anna often found herself operating in a more masculine energy space due to the lifestyle she was leading. For example, the type of positions she held at work called for her to operate in more of masculine space, however, when she was operating as a mother or wife she would switch to feminine energy. During the exploration of feminine versus masculine energy, she had spent a great deal of time learning how to ebb and flow between the two.

She first began to educate herself on this topic when she was trying to save her marriage to Lionel. One of her favorite authors on this topic is David Deida. He wrote a book titled, *The Way of the Superior Man* and *Dear Lover* and in both books, he explores the energy exchanges and importance of operating through each of these energies. *The Way of the Superior Man*, was written more so for men to read and *Dear Lover*, was written for a woman to read and understand a man's desires. Anna read both in an effort to get a deeper understanding of how she may be able to modify and/or alter her energies to be more pleasing to her partner, as they had really struggled in the area of him feeling as if she was not submissive enough and did not do as he expected.

Because Anna was so independent and predominantly operated in the masculine energy space in many areas of her life she was determined to learn, modify and adjust. Anna was always operating from a curiosity angle and maintained a flexible and adaptable mindset. She knew that if there was an issue, there was nothing that could not be solved with a little awareness and education. Deida's books provided a great deal of insight and really helped her to focus on intentionally exercising her feminine energy.

ENERGY FIELDS

Energy fields are a real thing. Our body emits energy, frequencies and vibrations. Around the body is an energy field that is unique to each person. The energy field can typically range as close as three feet and then expands out to six feet. For some, they are able to project their energy even further. So, if this is the case...why are we all so free flowing with our energy fields? Should we be more careful of who gets in our physical energetic space? It is interesting, because during the height of the pandemic, we were so careful about not getting within six feet of individuals in an attempt to safeguard and protect ourselves from contracting the virus. Applying this concept, should we be more careful with our energy? Not all energies are positive and being aware of who has access to and does not have access to our energy is really important. In instances, where energy is not protected it could be in jeopardy of being drained by energy vampires or those trying to do harm to someone. Once energy is drained, it must be restored or replenished, or the effects can be disastrous.

Anna learned this as she continued to experience a decline in her health. She found that being in toxic environments, where her energy was constantly being drained, had left her with nothing in reserve to allow her body, mind and spirit to restore itself and heal. Additionally, she recalled that Lionel would always attach his foot to her foot when they would sleep. At the time, she thought it was cute and romantic. It was not until she learned about energy that she realized that he would always touch her left foot with his foot when she would go to sleep, much like plugging an electric car into a charging port. She now knew that she was receiving his toxic, negative energy, which was essentially having a negative effect on her health.

Understanding energy and how the push and pull effect work were pivotal to Anna's healing journey. Previously she had walked through life leaving her energy field wide open for others to come and extract or deposit as they saw fit. She did not know how to protect her space, set boundaries verbally, physically and energetically. This was a problem that needed to be addressed immediately. You would not show up to battle without armor, so why was she showing up in life without protecting her energy field? The answer...she simply did not know about energetic fields and how profound the implications were when one is oblivious to such an important personal space.

She began learning tools and techniques to protect herself. From guided imagery to literally learning how to physically interact with others such as how to hug, which side of the body is the giving and the receiving, etc. There was so much information and science about this topic, and she jumped right in, eager to learn all that she could about the topic. She began practicing grounding and then establishing a routine to set intentions, protect her energy field and know when to remove herself from situations that threatened her sacred energy space.

Additionally, she began assessing who was in her life and who had access to her. If her body did not get a good vibe, she pulled back. It is not that everyone is necessarily good or bad, but she knew for her own sake that if she began to feel any bit of emotion that reminded her of less pleasant life experiences that it was time to pull back. She noticed that several people from her circle also began to disappear. It was simultaneously happening as her energetic vibrations increased, many of the lower vibrational people began to disappear from her circle. As difficult as this initially seemed for her, it was necessary to preserve her health and life.

Anna began to learn to trust during this process. She knew that God had heard and seen things that she could not and for that reason, the energetic field around her had elevated and it was time to up the ante. Anna was not here to continue more of the same, so learning and practicing energy safety and precautions became her new norm as she walked through each day. She became more trusting of her intuition and allowed her energetic responses to guide her as she proceeded to walk in her new path, purpose and gift!

ENERGY TECHNIQUES

During her journey, Anna was introduced to Rachel, by Stacey. Rachel and Anna quickly hit it off and began to get to know one another. Rachel had spent her entire career studying neuroscience and the effects of trauma on the body. She had devoted her life's work to uncovering techniques designed to assist individuals with moving stagnant energy that no longer served them out of their body. This allowed individuals to release blockages and restore the flow of current to a more consistent stable energetic response. Rachel had worked on Anna more than once and was able to uncover many inner wounds. She educated Anna on techniques to heal them by simply using Rachel's techniques and Anna's energetic field to push energy.

As Anna lay on Rachel's table, she would feel various sensations go through her body such as temperature changes, numbness and even felt the feeling of throat restriction that she had felt earlier during her medical crisis. As the movement and flow of energy, which was very inconsistent, continued, she could hear songs playing in her head and these songs were clues as to what was going on inside Anna's body and soul. It was during these sessions that Anna was able to uncover many truths she had not previously recognized and was able to address them through learning how to push the flow of energy through her body in a more consistent manner.

Another source of knowledge that Anna applied in this area were the techniques shared through Donna Eden's teachings. Her teachings provided insight into very practical daily routines to support energy flow and responses based on the individual's needs. She read and applied several of the techniques in Eden's book, *Energy Medicine*.

SOUND HEALING

Sound healing is an amazing modality that exists and needs to be shared with everyone everywhere! The benefits of sound healing sessions, whether at home, individual or group, are phenomenal. This approach provides the body with sounds and vibrations that speak to the soul...allowing for exchanges to occur between the conscious and subconscious. What a peaceful approach to healing.

Anna first experienced sound healing during one of her individual energy sessions with Nathan. It was so relaxing and soothing. She simply laid there on the table and heard the sounds of binaural beats, Tibetan sound bowls, chimes and the didgeridoo. Tuning forks were introduced during the session, as well, and were strategically focused on her chakras and meridian points requiring stabilization. She left the session feeling refreshed and overjoyed with the sense of calm that had washed over her. She felt grounded, mentally clear and at peace.

Up next...Anna decided to sign-up for the group Sound Bathing Sessions being offered.

What was so intriguing about these experiences was that Anna did not have to vocalize anything to the healers. The energetic vibrations did all of the talking. Anna found this to be extremely helpful, as traditional therapy required her to relive the stories and relive the trauma and she did not find this approach to be helpful for her mental health. She noticed it was requiring her to constantly relive the past and she did not want to relive the past, she wanted to move forward. Moving forward did require addressing the past to ensure she did not repeat patterns or behaviors, but constantly speaking about it did not wash it away. As she learned, often times, the subconscious does not know the difference between if something is happening now or if it is the past. As such, each time a memory is re-lived, it is felt emotionally as if it is the present time.

The Sound Bathing approach felt like an opportunity to hack the system and bypass the mainframe to allow for healing on a much deeper level. A level that required no words...just the feeling of vibrations that went straight to her core. Restoration of her mind, body, soul, DNA and her everything was all packed into these sessions.

ENERGY BEYOND THE PHYSICAL

After tragically losing her brother so suddenly, Anna began to explore what really happens during and after death. She understood that the body was left behind and the soul departs the physical human space. So, what does that mean? Anna realized that when her brother died, his physical human form was no longer one with which she could communicate. She recalled looking at his body lying in the hospital bed and feeling emptiness. She could physically see him, but realized he was not there.

It was during this time that she began to ask the questions. Where did his soul go? Where is he now? Is he gone forever? How can she communicate with him? She had seen her energy healer and she had made communication with him through that channel. She felt confident that really was him, because there were things that were said and revealed that no one could have possibly known. Then one day, during another energy session with another healer she asked, "How do you communicate when someone is in a non-physical form?" The answer was simple, yet profound. The response, "You would communicate with the person as if they were deaf and mute." Anna had to really ponder on what that meant. Soon after, she figured it out.

It was through energy that she could communicate with him. She was able to feel his presence. It was not like sitting and physically talking to him, but it was in the awareness that he was around. During this time, she had seen a healer who had done a reading on her and at the time, she recommended a book to her by Laura Lynne Jackson, *Signs*. It was after reading this book that Anna figured out just how to communicate with her brother using signs. It was a result of this experience that it was abundantly clear to Anna that energy fields extend well beyond the physical human energy field of three – six feet. Time and space are infinite, and she learned this even more when studying quantum physics and the teachings of Deepak Chopra, Bruce Lipton and Dr. Joe Dispenza.

TELEPATHIC ENERGY WORK

What an incredible experience! Telepathic communication is a divine gift that is absolutely astonishing. It is the communication between two or more beings that requires no words or formal communication. It is the ability to communicate through a spiritual connection that is independent of traditional communications. The ability to connect and communicate with another at the soul level is remarkable. During the process of telepathic energy work, energy can be transferred from one being to another without having to physically interact. This requires no physical constraints and can reach across time and space. Time and space are simply an illusion when using this technique.

Anna was blessed along her healing journey to learn and be a recipient of this form of energy healing. She received the blessing of healing energies being sent from a woman, Mary, who was very close to her. Mary would work on Anna from hundreds of miles away. It began slowly with Mary realizing her powers and gifts. Throughout the liver healing process Anna began struggling with wrapping her head around the fact that after so much healing there was still more damage she had to repair, which was from the horrific relationship she had left. It was like the wound that kept getting re-opened. Mary could sense this, so she quickly began to work on Anna during the late hours of night and early mornings. At first, Anna was not sure what was happening. She would wake up sweating like crazy in her sleep. When it first happened, she was not sure what was going on. She was on the phone with Mary. She asked if anything unusual happened that morning. Anna proceeded to share her experience of waking up in a sweat. Mary was extremely excited and began to share what she had done that morning to telepathically perform energy work on Anna.

The energy work Mary was performing was specifically targeting sweat glands in Anna's body from head to toe with the end goal of releasing toxins from her body. This would result in the increased rapid healing of Anna's liver. She continued to perform this work for several weeks. Doing so continued to assist Anna with her healing and sped up her weight loss journey as well.

THE JOURNEY...

Anna's journey is one that was necessary...necessary to experience, and necessary in order for her to share her story with others so that there can be an end to this vicious cycle of re- creation, of human pain and suffering. Her journey is nowhere near over! She has conquered so much pain and is still standing!

The message being sent through Anna's story of unintentional **RE-CREATION** and living in survival mode to **SURVIVE THE HUMAN EXPERIENCE**...is to let others know...IT IS TIME...TIME TO...

WAKE UP!!!

CONCLUDING THOUGHTS FROM ANNA...

We are all God's Children!

You can choose to walk your path with God at any point in your life...it is never too late!

You are part of the collective consciousness!

You...and you alone...need to reclaim your power!

Self-love is an essential ingredient in life!

Love heals all!

Boundaries are necessary!

Forgiveness is necessary for yourself...so that you may heal!

Protect your energy!

You have the ability to heal yourself!

You can change the course of your life at any given point in time!

Each day is a new day and an opportunity to create something new for yourself!

CALL TO ACTION...

**Re-Creation – Surviving the Human Experience
is a...**

CALL TO ACTION to HUMANS EVERYWHERE

AROUND THE GLOBE...

to begin the human experience of

AWAKENING...REMEMBERING...

RECLAIMING YOUR POWER AND...

TO LIVE YOUR TRUTH!!!

Made in United States
North Haven, CT
30 June 2023

38420356R00114